BOMBS, BOMBINGS
& BOMB DISPOSAL
STUDY GUIDE

by

THOMAS G. BRODIE

and

RALPH E. HENDEL

Based on two outstanding textbooks:

BOMBS AND BOMBINGS
by Thomas G. Brodie

and

EXPLOSIVES AND BOMB DISPOSAL GUIDE
by Robert R. Lenz

Both of these texts are published by
C. C. THOMAS, Springfield, Illinois

TABLE OF CONTENTS

INTRODUCTION

With this book we welcome a new writer to our group of experts. Thomas G. Brodie, the author of the book "Bombs and Bombings," is well-known in the field of bomb technology. He has safely and effectively handled many infernal devices, and has handled many bomb investigations. An inventor, he devised the first top-vented bomb carrier. He has been decorated by the British government with the M.B.E. (Member of the Most Excellent Order of the British Empire).

He is now a consultant to the National Bomb Data Center, and is well-known as a lecturer, training officer, and consultant and participant in bomb technology seminars.

We are honored to have him as part of our staff.

With this book we also welcome again Lt. Ralph E. Hendel, who prepared the questions on "Explosives and Bomb Disposal Guide," by Robert R. Lenz. Once more, his questions bring out succinctly and accurately the important items in the book.

This book also represents a "first" for our firm; this is the first time we have presented questions covering two books in one of our study guides. We have done this because the material is so closely allied between the two books, and because we feel it necessary for the student to be well aware of all the information contained in the two books.

STEWART T. DAVIS, President

BOMBS AND BOMBINGS

Fundamental statements on disposal and investigation of recovered explosives and bombs and bombings can not be overemphasized.

1. All reports of bombs should be treated as bona-fide reports until proved otherwise.

2. All bombs which are found which have not exploded are potentially very hazardous. So rather than rush in and, right or wrong, do something, be careful NOT to do anything which may set off the bomb. YOUR LIFE is much more important than any evidence you may discover, or any property you may save by attempting to disarm or remove the bomb, UNLESS YOU KNOW EXACTLY WHAT YOU ARE DOING IN EACH INSTANCE.

3. In some instances, bombs, whether exploded or unexploded, are intended to carry a message to someone connected with the incident. They may be intended to carry a message of vulnerability to bombing; by killing someone to warn a group of people of a hazard to them, etc.

4. When bombs have exploded, those in close proximity to the explosion, even if apparently not seriously injured, should be very closely examined by medical personnel; in some cases punctured eardrums are not immediately found. In other cases tumors in lungs, etc., may show up at long intervals afterward and eventually found to be directly connected to the explosion.

5. Bombs may be exploded in many different ways: through contact; by movement, up, down, to the right, to the left, forward, backward, or by any combination of movements; by pressure; by release of pressure; by time mechanism; by release of "booby trap" mechanism; by remote control, etc.

6. Often there is more than one bomb at a scene; often the detonation of the first is to draw a crowd, so that the second may be detonated with more killing or terrifying effect — or even a third one may be present.

7. The bomb which has been found by a citizen and picked up and brought to the fire or police station is much more hazardous than the one which has been found and is left in place; merely picking up the bomb and transporting it may activate a time device which will cause the bomb to explode minutes or hours later.

8. Bombs are the coward's way of being deadly; their effect is not so much the actual damage done, but the fear or anticipation of damage to be done by the repetition of the act in the future.

9. A bomb may be placed, dropped, thrown, or projected; the area to be searched for evidence must therefore include (unless method of delivery is known) a larger area than is required for most criminal acts.

1

10. DON'T PANIC. Your actions must follow certain routines which have been developed by successful technicians through trial and error, and loss of life, to determine the correct routines.

CITIZEN RESPONSIBILITY

If a citizen finds what he believes is a bomb, he has certain responsibilities: 1. DO NOT APPROACH THE BOMB; 2. fix its exact location in his mind, so he can direct bomb disposal specialists to it without delay; 3. if possible without endangering himself by getting too close to the bomb note its physical appearance, so he can describe it to the person who needs to know this information — it may save someone's life, and certainly will speed up action; 4. take note of what kind of detonating device it appears to have — are there wires running from it, or an apparent cord or fuse; 5. how large is it; 6. of what does it appear to be composed — dynamite or other type of explosive, liquid, etc.

If found by a group of people, all but one should immediately leave the area; one or two should take proper cover and be prepared to warn any late-comers not to walk into the danger area. The ones who left the area should immediately call either the fire department or the police agency for the area, and report as full and complete information about the incident as possible.

DUTIES OF THE OFFICER RECEIVING THE REPORT

The officer receiving the report will receive it from one of three sources: 1) the citizen who found the bomb; 2) a citizen who received a call from someone else about the bomb; or 3) the person who placed the bomb or who wants to initiate the bomb scare.

If the call is from a person who actually found a bomb or a suspected bomb, he should be asked the questions under "citizen responsibility" above; if he has merely been the recipient of a bomb threat from an anonymous caller, the citizen should be asked for all possible information about the call — the exact words of the caller, any background noises heard (traffic, music, or laughter, etc.); an opinion as to the sex, age, voice accent, attitude, speech impediment, etc., of the caller. Of course, the caller should be held on the line, if possible, to answer these questions while the officer receiving the report dispatches someone to the scene.

If the officer receives an anonymous bomb threat, he should ask the caller:

1. What is the exact location of the bomb?
2. What does the bomb look like?
3. What will make it explode?
4. How do we get rid of it?
5. Why was it put there?

In the meantime, the officer should initiate any local means to "lock in" the call, so that the location from which it is being made can be determined. If equipment is available, the call should be taped. Any

2

trace of emotion — fear, anger, panic, etc. — should be kept out of the officer's voice, if at all possible. Many bomb calls appear to be made for the shock effect apparent upon the recipients of the call.

DUTIES OF THE FIRST OFFICER ON THE SCENE

1.   DO NOT REPORT YOUR ARRIVAL BY RADIO! This might detonate the bomb, if there is actually one present. It is usually best to locate the area where the bomb has been reported; if it is seen, then follow up with the procedure which seems most appropriate to the incident. Usually the first thing to do is to order the immediate evacuation of all persons to a place which is a safe distance from the bomb's suspected location. This should be at least 300 feet from the potential point of the explosion — farther if possible. Protective barriers (walls, etc., vehicles) may lessen the required distance. Warn bystanders to stay away from windows, as explosions breaking the glass may lead to bad lacerations.

2.   UNDER NO CIRCUMSTANCES SHOULD THE UN-TRAINED POLICE OFFICER OR FIRE FIGHTER TOUCH A SUSPECTED BOMB OR EXPLOSIVE!

Leave this to the bomb squad. To put it simply, MOVE THE PEOPLE AWAY FROM THE BOMB, NOT THE BOMB AWAY FROM THE PEOPLE.

Be prepared to render first aid if necessary, and above all pay particular note to who is at the scene. Be on the alert for possible suspects or witnesses. If possible, photograph the bystanders — the suspect may later be identified as being at the scene.

Be prepared to answer questions from the bomb disposal or backup unit: why do you think it is a bomb? Where is it? Has it been moved? Where did it come from? What is it suspected of being? When was it first discovered? Who discovered it? What is the apparent reason for setting the bomb?

DUTIES OF BACK-UP UNIT AND SUPERVISOR

Duties of this group are just what the title indicates: they should "back up" or assist the lead unit. They should assist in crowd control, identification of bomb, search for bomb, etc. The supervisor should estimate the situation and advise his headquarters of any further needs.

When the crowd has been evacuated and is under control, the next problem is to actually find the bomb — if it is not immediately visible. There are several different ways in which to accomplish this. It must be remembered that there are many businesses which are totally dependent upon customer flow; to keep them closed down is going to cause them to go out of business. The persons who normally are inside a building (if a building is involved) are best qualified to note anything unusual in the way of a package. Sometimes it is going to be best to allow one person per room to reenter the scene and try to locate any strange object. Ths is a calculated risk, as the bomb may go off (if one is actually present) at any time. Those permitted to re-enter the scene should be advised not to touch the strange object, but immediately report it to the public safety personnel present.

For safety and expediency searches for bombs are best performed by employees or inhabitants of the location. The primary reasons for employee search is that they are more familiar with the area than strangers (police, firemen or other employees) and know what should be there and what should not be there. The employees are advised beforehand that they are not bomb disposal specialists and are only making sure that a bomb is not near them and under no circumstances are they to touch "something that doesn't belong" or they "don't know what it is."

Check lists of rooms and individual areas, floor plans of the building, etc., if available, will assist in planning the search.

If your department is large enough to have an explosives and ordnance disposal squad, you will undoubtedly have had instruction in what your particular squad wants you to do in a given situation, and they will be called to duty as soon as the threat is received. If, however, you are dependent upon the military for such assistance, you must remember that often THEY WILL NOT COME TO THE SCENE UNTIL YOU HAVE ACTUALLY LOCATED AND IDENTIFIED A BOMB! Since this situation exists in 95% of all the departments in the United States, the search becomes a major problem.

No more people than the absolute minimum should be permitted in the search area. Other public safety personnel should be ready to give first aid, if required, or to furnish any additional assistance required. Remember, search for the bomb may be very boring, but the object of planting bombs is often to get the searchers to reduce their attention, and to catch them unaware.

The most common locations for bombs to be placed are: the outside of the building, the entrance, the first floor, bathrooms or rest rooms, storerooms, and waste receptacles. Custodians should play a large part in searches, since they are familiar with, and usually have keys to, many rooms that are seldom used.

Don't forget: a bomb scare is often initiated in order to secure police or fire commitment to an area, leaving another area uncovered. The uncovered area may be the object of a burglary, or an arson fire. So, as public safety personnel are pulled out of an area, they should be replaced as soon as possible, by back-up personnel. Fire department personnel are usually better for searching than are police because they are usually available in larger groups, with ladders, tools, lights, and other equipment that may be needed in the search.

WHEN A BOMB HAS BEEN FOUND, DO NOT GIVE UP THE SEARCH. Possibly one is placed where it can be easily found, and another one slated to do more damage is well-hidden. Occasionally, too, the first one is placed where it can be easily located so that more public safety personnel will be congregated near there, and make the effect of a second one more deadly. The first bomb may be connected by some booby-trap mechanism to the second bomb so that an attempt to disarm or dismantle the first bomb will activate the second one.

DON'T THINK ONLY IN TERMS OF A PACKAGED TIME BOMB WHEN CONDUCTING A SEARCH. The bomb may be a booby-trapped package, or a booby-trap attached to anything movable — a door, window, furniture, toilet seat, etc. Types of search must be changed, and procedures will have to be changed, with different types of areas to be searched. Vehicles, hospitals, schools, airplanes, theaters, stores — all of them have special problems to be anticipated in the search.

Bombers have called police if they have had a misfire — and then follow it up with another bomb which does not misfire. False bomb reports often precede actual bomb events, as well.

Even if the search is extremely slow, don't get jittery about the commitment of personnel to the search area. Finding the bomb safely, and handling it properly, are much more important than speed; speed can cause injuries and deaths, so take your time, be thorough, and be SURE you cover the entire area where a bomb could be hidden.

WHAT ABOUT NEWS COVERAGE?

News coverage should be a mutual decision between the public safety department and the news media and the manager. Consideration should be given to the possibility that the bomb scare is initiated to secure publicity for a radical political view. Publicity may be the only thing desired, and frustration of this desire may cause the bomber to reveal himself through more overt activities, and further calls to law enforcement agencies or fire departments. Sometimes, though, the necessity for informing the public is paramount; to alert the public concerning the existence of a bomber in the area may lead to someone reporting suspicious activity which may indicate the identity of the responsible. This should be considered by both the media and the public safety official in charge of the scene.

WHAT ABOUT TOP LEVEL ADMINISTRATIVE ACTION?

During all this time the top level administrators are planning support activities, as well as arranging for (if necessary) additional personnel to cover vacant police beats or vacant fire houses. They are also handling the many activities connected with publicity, public relations, reassurance of the public, etc. If equipment must be borrowed from some other jurisdiction, it is being arranged for; bomb disposal trailers, carriers, armor, etc., may need to be brought in from fairly distant points, and it is urgent that it be started on its way as rapidly as possible.

ADDITIONAL INFORMATION.

When commercial explosives are reported to a law enforcement organization, and there is any question about whether or not they are deteriorated, or when there is any question about the safety of undertaking to handle them, a representative of the manufacturer of the particular lot of explosives should be consulted or a request for assistance made to an authorized representative of the U. S. Bureau of Mines, of the Department of the Interior, or to someone else known to have had the necessary experience and knowledge.

Shells of blasting caps that have been wet and then dried may show signs of corrosion. These caps may be VERY DANGEROUS to handle, and it is recommended that they NOT BE DISTURBED until a representative of the manufacturer has had an opportunity to pass on them.

The popular idea that any bomb should be immersed in water is highly dangerous.

Water might cause initiation of some explosives, complete an electrical circuit necessary to detonate a bomb and is entirely ineffective in other types of bombs when the explosive may be enclosed in a glass jar, or as in the case of dynamite, wrapped in a waterproof wrapper.

Acetone is a universal solvent for all explosives except black powder. Black powder is disabled by immersion in water and water may stop a clock mechanism.

The standard burning rate for safety fuse in general use is 120 seconds per yard. Detonating fuse, which may be confused with safety fuse by the uninformed, burns at the rate of 20,000 feet per second.

The ordinary function of a private citizen who discovers a bomb or suspected bomb is merely to warn all persons from the area and to notify the proper authorities.

An officer, however, in addition to the items mentioned in most articles, should: establish an organized guard (either law enforcement or civilian) outside the danger area; arrange for medical aid to stand by; shut off power, gas, and fuel lines leading into the danger area; remove flammable materials from the surrounding area; notify the local fire department and rescue squad; obtain the services of a competent explosives expert; obtain mattresses to be used as protection against flying fragments; check and have available fire extinguishing equipment; and arrange for the use of portable X-ray equipment.

If an explosion has already occurred, be sure to cover these items in interrogating possible witnesses: What was the sound of the explosion? What was the force of the explosion and its direction? What was the color of smoke? What was the odor of the gases produced? What was the color of the flame?

ADDITIONAL SOURCES OF INFORMATION ON BOMBS, EXPLOSIVES, AND PLANNING

Much additional information may be obtained from the following articles and books concerning this general subject:

USDJ, FBI Bulletins of April, 1953, August, 1955, September, 1957, September and October, 1959, and April, 1971.

FEDERAL REGISTER, Vol. 36, Number 10, dated Friday, January 15, 1971, Part II, DEPARTMENT OF THE TREASURY, Internal Revenue Service: Part 181, Commerce in Explosives (Pub. 739) and Explosives List.

ARSON INVESTIGATION, pamphlet prepared by the Arson Detail, Las Vegas Fire Department, undated.

EXPLOSIVES AND BOMB DISPOSAL GUIDE, pamphlet prepared by Las Vegas Fire Department, Arson Detail, undated.

BOMBS, EXPLOSIVES AND INCENDIARY DEVICES, by Richard A. Durfee, published by Police Science Press, P. O. Box 1468, Cocoa Beach, Florida (1961).

EXPLOSIVES AND HOMEMADE BOMBS, by Major Joseph F. Stoffel, distributed by Davis Publishing Company, 250 Potrero Street, Santa Cruz, California 95060

EXPLOSIVES AND BOMB DISPOSAL GUIDE, by Robert R. Lenz,, distributed by Davis Publishing Company, 250 Potrero Street, Santa Cruz, California 95060

DESTRUCTION OF DAMAGED, DETERIORATED, OR UNWANTED COMMERCIAL EXPLOSIVES, U. S. Bureau of Mines Information Circular 7335.

BOMB SEARCH PLANNING, by Thomas G. Brodie and Dee Feldstein, Motorola Teleprograms, Schiller Park, Illinois.

In addition to the foregoing, some information on the use of trained dogs to sniff out bombs may be obtained from the Washington, D.C. Police Department, and from the Capitol Police, Washington, D.C.

BOMBS AND BOMBINGS

Questions and answers may be verified from "Bombs & Bombings," by Thomas G. Brodie.

1. Upon finding an object suspected of being a bomb a police officer should first:

   (A) make sure the item is a bomb
   (B) listen for ticking; or look for smoke
   (C) call for the bomb squad
   (D) see what kind of explosive is in the bomb

2. The initiating system of a bomb may be found:

   (A) on the side or middle of the explosive
   (B) separate from the explosive
   (C) on top of the explosive
   (D) under the explosive
   (E) all of the above

3. Planning for future bomb reports and scares by law enforcement groups is often undertaken:
    (A) when there are many newspaper reports of bomb incidents
    (B) when nearby departments have had reported incidents
    (C) after a bomb incident has occurred in their own jurisdiction
    (D) after an injury following a bomb incident in their own jurisdiction

4. A tactical plan means a plan for:
    (A) special situations
    (B) staff procedure
    (C) line operations
    (D) daily standard operating procedure
    (E) none of the above

5. A small police department may obtain more equipment and training for bombs than they will need because:
    (A) they panic because of one incident they had
    (B) they want to enhance their image
    (C) of poor rapport with another police bomb squad
    (D) they think more of someone's property than their own lives
    (E) all of the above

6. The first decision to be made concerning precautionary measures for bomb incident control is:
    (A) who should undertake the training
    (B) who should be trained
    (C) what should be covered in the training
    (D) who should do the training
    (E) who is going to dispose of a bomb if one is found

7. What is the best guarantee for safety of the person responsible for bomb disposal:
    (A) experience
    (B) armor and protective equipment
    (C) training
    (D) calm and analytical judgment under emergency condtions

8. It is probably best for the small department to:
    (A) purchase elaborate equipment with which to deal with possible bomb incidents
    (B) consider outside assistance; pooling equipment with other small departments in some central location
    (C) make plans to "do something themselves" even if what they do is the wrong thing
    (D) train all their people as bomb disposal experts

9. The final decision of what to do with a suspected bomb should be made by:

    (A)   the bomb disposal specialist
    (B)   the ranking officer at the scene
    (C)   the precinct captain
    (D)   the fire chief in charge of the scene
    (E)   an agreement between the bomb specialist and his superior officer

10. Which of the following groups constitute one of the biggest problems within a department:

    (A)   officers not assigned to the bomb squad but who have been in the armed forces or had limited experience in blasting
    (B)   civilians whose curiosity is aroused and believe "I was in the service and know all about explosives"
    (C)   those who, through lack of experience (children, etc.) fail to recognize a bomb and pick it up to handle it
    (D)   all of the above are problem groups who constitute the biggest problems for a department

11. Which of the following is NOT ordinarily a duty of the Federal Bureau of Investigation with reference to bomb incidents:

    (A)   upon request of the local department, to collect evidence and conduct criminal investigations
    (B)   through the facilities of the laboratory in Washington, D.C., to examine bombing evidence submitted to them and report their findings
    (C)   to dispose of bombs found
    (D)   all of the foregoing are duties of the FBI

12. Explosive ordnance disposal (EOD) personnel from the Armed Services will:

    (A)   respond on every request by the local police
    (B)   respond on military ordnance but not homemade bombs
    (C)   respond depending on the policy of their base commander
    (D)   respond on military ordnance but not homemade bombs

13. From which of the following organizations having explosive-trained personnel with equipment, is it impossible to secure disposal service for bombs found:

    (A)   United States Secret Service
    (B)   explosive ordnance personnel (EOD) from any of the U. S. Army Headquarters in the Continental U. S.
    (C)   EOD personnel from local Air Force bases
    (D)   EOD personnel from Navy bases

14. Which of the following are limitations and problems in obtaining assistance by the Armed Services:

(A) time involved in obtaining permission from the commanding officer and travel from the nearest base
(B) Posse comitatus, in which Armed Forces cannot be used for public functions such as searching for bombs or searching for evidence
(C) distant assignment elsewhere or discharge from the service before needed for court appearance
(D) inexperience with homemade bombs, bomb-scene investigation, evidence, and court testimony
(E) all the foregoing

15. Police and fire departments can obtain dummy commercial explosives displays from:

(A) the Bureau of Mines
(B) the International Association of Chiefs of Police
(C) the National Bomb Data Center
(D) the Institute of Makers of Explosives

16. The safest way to learn bomb disposal is:

(A) on the job training
(B) attending the hazardous devices school at Redstone
(C) reading and practicing
(D) attending seminars

17. Which of the following is no longer a source of training in explosives:

(A) explosive companies, names of which will be furnished upon request by the Institute of the Makers of Explosives, 420 Lexington Avenue, N.Y. 10017
(B) Army Explosive Disposal Control 2½-day schools for local police and fire departments
(C) experienced police bomb squads of larger departments
(D) independent bomb instructors, names of whom can be furnished by IACP, Washington, D.C.
(E) the combined Justice Department/U.S. Army 3-week school at Redstone Arsenal, Alabama

18. The most complete literature on bomb disposal can be obtained from:

(A) conversation with a bomb disposal specialist
(B) the National Bomb Data Center
(C) United States Army Field Manuals
(D) there is'nt much information on the subject

19. Which is an advantage of having a few members of a bomb squad work together instead of distribution of men throughout the department:

    (A) training and experience and development of specialists
    (B) control and safety
    (C) care of equipment
    (D) knowledge of every other specialists' work
    (E) all of the above

20. Which of the following statements is incorrect:

    (A) for departments smaller than New York Police Department, there is not enough business to keep one man occupied completely on bomb disposal work
    (B) the members of a bomb squad for any department should all be in the same unit with similar assignments instead of being spread out in the department with dissimilar secondary duties
    (C) a one-man bomb squad, in a small department, is adequate
    (D) three or four men should be the size of the bomb squad for any department, as one of them can always be on call and available

21. Which of the following statements is incorrect:

    (A) the purpose of a bomb carrier is to transport a bomb safely from the location where it was found to a location where it can be stored, deactivated, dismantled, or blown
    (B) dismantling an open or partly open bomb may be simple
    (C) disarming a closed bomb is quite risky
    (D) all bombs, given a knowledgeable technician, can be deactivated
    (E) a bomb carrier takes away much of the risk to a novice bomb technician

22. The first successful bomb carrier was developed in:

    (A) 1914 by Professor Kling of the Paris Laboratory
    (B) 1920 by New York City after the Wall Street Bombing
    (C) 1942 by New York City after the 1940 World's Fair bombing
    (D) 1946 by the United States Secret Service in Washington, D.C.

23. The simplest method of bomb removal for the novice bomb technician is:

    (A)   explode it in place by placing a controlled explosive against it and exploding it, so the bomb will go off by sympathetic reaction

    (B)   use a remote-control device to place the bomb in a carrier and remove it to a safe place to detonate it

    (C)   find the triggering device and place safety device over it

    (D)   dismantle it where found

24. There are .... basic types of bomb carriers. The number which most accurately fills the blank is:

    (A)   two
    (B)   three
    (C)   four
    (D)   five

25. The first top vented bomb carrier was designed and tested successfully by:

    (A)   the Dade County Public Safety Department in 1961
    (B)   the Metropolitan Toronto Police Department in 1962
    (C)   the Nassau County Police Department in 1965
    (D)   the National Bomb Data Center in 1971

26. In considering the type of bomb carrier to be used, which of the following are major considerations:

    (A)   whether carrier should be a truck or a trailer
    (B)   whether the carrier should be topless and bottomless or merely topless
    (C)   the weight of the carrier
    (D)   ease of handling and speed of driving capability
    (E)   all the foregoing

27. The duration of an explosion is less than:

    (A)   1 second
    (B)   2 seconds
    (C)   3 seconds
    (D)   4 seconds

28. An explosion travels in which direction:

    (A)   up
    (B)   down
    (C)   sideways
    (D)   the path of least resistance or in all directions

29. The advantage of a truck bomb carrier over a trailer carrier is:

   (A) easier to drive
   (B) no concern over engine breakdown
   (C) more than one vehicle can be used to tow it
   (D) vehicle is not in use elsewhere

30. The complainant or police officer's identification as to the type of explosive or bomb is:

   (A) often wrong
   (B) often right
   (C) always wrong
   (D) always right

31. If a bomb carrier is available, it should:

   (A) be kept in a central yard until the need for it has been determined
   (B) be hooked up to tow vehicle immediately upon receipt of the call
   (C) taken along with the bomb technician as soon as call is received
   (D) follow along as rapidly as possible, being driven by some-one from the corporation yard

32. The most commonly used tools by the bomb specialists are:

   (A) X-ray machine and fluoroscope
   (B) line, knife and wire cutter
   (C) bomb carrier and bomb suit
   (D) galvanometer and blasting machine

33. Of the following statements: (1) in addition to the bomb carrier, certain equipment is urgently needed; (2) needed equipment is of two types — expendable and non-expendable:

   (A) both statements are true
   (B) statement #1 is true, #2 is false
   (C) statement #2 is true, #1 is false
   (D) both statements are false

34. Blasting caps are:

   (A) not carried in a bomb vehicle because of radios
   (B) carried in a blasting kit with C4 in a bomb vehicle
   (C) carried in a blasting kit separate from C4
   (D) none of the above

35. The most expensive piece of equipment on a bomb truck is:

   (A) galvanometer
   (B) nitroglycerine desensitizer
   (C) X-ray machine
   (D) non-sparking tools

36. Nitroglycerin desensitizer consists of:

    (A) acetone, alcohol, sodium sulphide and water
    (B) silver nitrate solution and iodine
    (C) water and acetone
    (D) potassium chlorate and sugar

37. A steam explosion is classified as a:

    (A) mechanical explosion
    (B) chemical explosion
    (C) nuclear explosion
    (D) none of the above

38. An implosion is:

    (A) the opposite of an explosion
    (B) a bursting inward
    (C) a collapsing of a vacuum
    (D) what occurs following an explosion
    (E) all of the above

39. An explosion is described as a sudden going from one place to another and is illustrated by:

    (A) a sudden violent action by a person
    (B) a rapid expansion of gas
    (C) a piece of machinery broken loose by centrifugal force
    (D) a sudden exclamation of speech
    (E) all of the above

40. The types of explosion are which of the following: 1, steam or mechanical; 2, chemical; and 3, nuclear:

    (A) all of the above
    (B) #1
    (C) #2
    (D) #3
    (E) #2 and #3 are the only types of concern to the bomb technician

41. Which statement is incorrect?

    (A) An explosion must be accompanied by a loud report.
    (B) An explosion must be a sudden movement.
    (C) Implosions follow explosions.
    (D) There are only three types of explosions.

42. Which of the following is not part of the "explosion triangle" indicated in the text "Bombs and Bombings," by Thomas G. Brodie:

    (A) fuel (carbon)
    (B) oxygen (potassium chlorate)
    (C) heat
    (D) motion

43. The differences between a fire and an explosion are:

    (A) a fire must contain its own oxygen, but an explosion draws its oxygen from the air
    (B) a fire is much slower than an explosion in its effect; some explosions take place in as little as three milli-seconds
    (C) in the production of an explosive, fuel must be mixed with oxygen
    (D) all the foregoing are true
    (E) B and C are true; A is false

44. Chemical explosions have a duration of:

    (A) microseconds
    (B) nanoseconds
    (C) milliseconds
    (D) seconds

45. Which of the following is true:

    (A) Upon the evaporation of gasoline its danger is lessened.
    (B) Gasoline vapors may be ignited by a match.
    (C) Gasoline vapors are easily seen.
    (D) A flame must touch the liquid gasoline to ignite it.

46. These chemicals are used to manufacture nitroglycerine:

    (A) sulfuric acid, nitric acid and glycerine
    (B) sawdust and glycerine
    (C) fertilizer, soap and acid
    (D) ethylene glycol and nitric acid

47. This explosive is the same thing as dynamite:

    (A) TNT
    (B) RDX
    (C) PETN
    (D) HMX
    (E) none of the above

48. Hypergolic means:
    (A)   the explosive will gather moisture from the air
    (B)   an over balance of glycerine in nitroglycerine
    (C)   the explosive is self initiating
    (D)   a fast velocity explosive
    (E)   none of the above

49. Which is true of low velocity explosives:
    (A)   the greater the heat, the greater the pressure
    (B)   when heat increases the pressure lessens
    (C)   the faster the explosive burns the less heat is produced
    (D)   none of the above

50. The main reason black powder is usually found in pipe bombs is:
    (A)   increased heat and pressure
    (B)   concealment
    (C)   fragmentation
    (D)   convenience in carrying

51. Which of the following statements about explosives is incorrect:
    (A)   all explosives require initiation by heat or shock
    (B)   some explosives are so sensitive to heat that they explode as a result of being mixed together
    (C)   confining a lower-velocity explosive increases the velocity of the explosion
    (D)   hypergolic explosives explode as a result of being mixed together
    (E)   none of the foregoing is incorrect

52. Which of the following are the two types of blasting caps:
    (A)   fulminate of mercury and lead azide
    (B)   electric and fuse
    (C)   heat sensitive explosive with pressure-sensitive base charge explosive
    (D)   shock and heat

53. Which of the following is the best definition of a bomb:
    (A)   a bomb is an explosive device designed to explode in a specific manner
    (B)   a bomb is an explosive substance which is delivered with the unlawful intention of causing injury, death, destruction of property, or creating a disturbance
    (C)   a bomb is an infernal machine
    (D)   a bomb is an explosive in a container, with a method of exploding it attached

54. The venturi is:

   (A)   window
   (B)   the initiating system of a rocket
   (C)   the target
   (D)   shattering effect of an explosive
   (E)   none of the above

55. In how many fashions may a bomb be planted or set:

   (A)   two
   (B)   three
   (C)   four
   (D)   five

56. What is a limpit mine:

   (A)   a mine which is so heavy it causes the bearer or carrier of it to limp
   (B)   one which has no rigidity
   (C)   one which has been put together in a lime pit
   (D)   an explosive charge that is to be attached by adhesive tape or other device to its target

57. The advantages of a "good" bomb as pointed out by extremist groups are:

   (A)   it destroys all the evidence
   (B)   the perpetrator can be miles away when his bomb explodes
   (C)   the bomber can select his type of bomb for his particular reason
   (D)   all of the above

58. What is an "open bomb:"

   (A)   a bomb in which the means of initiation and explosive can be seen
   (B)   a bomb found in an open field
   (C)   a bomb found in an open area, such as outside a building
   (D)   any of the foregoing

59. Which of the following is not an advantage of a bomb as a weapon:

   (A)   a good bomb destroys all the evidence of type, manufacture, and delivery
   (B)   a good bomb permits the bomber to be miles away when it explodes
   (C)   an innocent person may explode a booby-trap bomb
   (D)   all the foregoing make the bomb an excellent weapon

17

60. Which of the following is a method of initiating the explosion of a bomb:

 (A) timed control
 (B) motion
 (C) remote control
 (D) all the foregoing

61. In the United States, the most common method of initiating the explosion of a bomb is:

 (A) timed control
 (B) motion
 (C) remote control
 (D) a combination of two of the three methods

62. A collapsing circuit is:

 (A) a dud bomb
 (B) a bomb with a faulty electrical connection
 (C) a relay device or battery decay
 (D) a corrosive chemical collapsing or breaking a membrane to a hypergolic chemical train

63. Which of the following is not a type of time delay for a bomb:

 (A) burning
 (B) corrosive
 (C) remote control
 (D) electrical
 (E) mechanical

64. Over 50% of the United States casualties in Viet Nam were caused by:

 (A) Chinese time pencils
 (B) booby traps
 (C) fragmentation of explosive artillery shells
 (D) time bombs in Saigon

65. The most common type of delay device is:

 (A) burning black powder fuse
 (B) corrosive delay (an acid eating through a metal separating medium to a chemical that explodes on contact with the acid)
 (C) electrical time bomb
 (D) mechanical delay

18

66. The most common type of initiation of booby-trap or package type of bomb is:

   (A) burning black powder
   (B) corrosive
   (C) motion
   (D) electric

67. Motion initiated bombs are regulated by:

   (A) direction of motion
   (B) speed of motion
   (C) distance of motion
   (D) all of the above

68. Anti-disturbance devices found on bombs are of which of the following types:

   (A) pull
   (B) tension release
   (C) pressure
   (D) pressure release
   (E) all the foregoing

69. In initiation of a bomb by remote control, which of the following is not a usual method:

   (A) burning
   (B) electronic
   (C) electrical
   (D) mechanical

70. Consider these statements: 1) a Molotov cocktail explodes; 2) an incendiary device composed of hypergolic chemicals that burn upon mixing is an explosive:

   (A) both statements are true
   (B) the first is true; the second is false
   (C) the second is true; the first is false
   (D) both statements are false

71. A Molotov cocktail is classified as:

   (A) an incendiary
   (B) a bomb
   (C) an explosive device that burns
   (D) all of the above

19

72. Two or more chemical elements or compounds that burn or explode as a result of the heat of the chemical reaction upon being mixed or compounded, immediately, or later are:

   (A) the statement is false; no such materials exist
   (B) hypergolic
   (C) hygroscopic
   (D) hydrostatic

73. An "expert" is defined by the dictionary as:

   (A) someone who knows all of the answers
   (B) someone with a briefcase from the next county
   (C) "ex" meaning was and "spert" as a drip of water
   (D) someone with a great deal of knowledge of a certain subject

74. What makes a man a "bomb expert" for Court purposes:

   (A) a thorough course of training
   (B) a great deal of experience with bombs
   (C) a decision of the Court
   (D) a bomb specialist who has studied for many years

75. Which of the following is not a common way for bombers to obtain their explosives:

   (A) buying them
   (B) stealing them
   (C) making them
   (D) all the former are frequently-used methods of obtaining explosives

76. The best procedure to follow when a dynamite fire is found burning is:

   (A) extinguish the flames with water
   (B) smother the fire with sand
   (C) evacuate the area
   (D) none of the above

77. The main use of commercial explosives is to:

   (A) move stumps
   (B) break rock so that it can be moved more easily with machines
   (C) munitions
   (D) bombing

78. The best procedure for regulation of explosives is:

   (A) laissez faire
   (B) stringent laws
   (C) practical enforcement laws
   (D) none of the above

79. Laws governing the use of explosives require:

   (A) sufficient enforcement personnel
   (B) seismographs to test the efficiency of explosives
   (C) cooperation of blasters and the local citizens
   (D) all of the above

80. A blaster's helper is called:

   (A) a powder monkey
   (B) dynamite stick
   (C) straight man
   (D) capper

81. When investigating dynamite explosions it is:

   (A) difficult to determine relative positions of victims because victims are usually too mutilated to tell much
   (B) usually easy to determine relative positions of victims because the side of the victim facing the center of the explosion is more severely damaged
   (C) difficult to determine which way a person was facing because vacuum effect causes damage on all sides of the body equivalent to the force exerted by the explosion
   (D) none of the above statements are true

82. The stealing of dynamite is similar to what other type of crime:

   (A) extortion
   (B) car theft
   (C) the theft of a truck load of guns
   (D) homicide

83. In most areas of the country, ... per cent of dynamite thefts result in bombings. The figure which most accurately fills the blank is:

   (A) 50
   (B) 75
   (C) 90
   (D) 100

84. A frequent cause of injury and death in blasting accidents is:

 (A) faulty manufacture of fuse causing "hot spots" that burn faster than normal
 (B) the blaster cutting his fuse too short
 (C) the blaster kinking or bending the fuse too sharply
 (D) the use of old fuse which burns faster than new fuse

85. A motive for the theft of explosives may be for:

 (A) breaking into areas where money is stored
 (B) revenge
 (C) revolution
 (D) all of the above

86. In estimating the amount of explosives used, results of known amounts and types of explosives which exploded in the past show:

 (A) the amount of explosive is unimportant
 (B) the position of the explosive is unimportant
 (C) the type of explosive is unimportant
 (D) all of the above statements are false

87. Which statement about the use of electric blasting caps is false:

 (A) The blaster should hook up his blasting machine to the circuit before he hooks up his cap.
 (B) Use a galvanometer to check his circuit before he hooks up his cap or blasting machine.
 (C) Never connect his blasting machine into the circuit before he hooks up his cap.
 (D) Never pull his blasting wires after he has connected his cap.

88. Which answer is most nearly correct? Settling causes what type of cracks in structures:

 (A) "X"
 (B) linear and/or vertical
 (C) linear
 (D) vertical

89. Bomb threats, bombings of aircrafts, ships, and interstate commerce, are handled by:

 (A) local police departments
 (B) Alcohol Tax Unit of Internal Revenue Service
 (C) Federal Bureau of Investigation
 (D) Whichever department receives the call first

90. The United States Senate committee that investigated the revolutionary bombings in 1969 and 1970 was the:
    (A) McGraw Hill
    (B) Johnson Nixon
    (C) McClellan
    (D) Escobedo

91. In the preparation of any tactical plan concerning bomb scares, which of the following should be considered:
    (A) evacuation
    (B) search
    (C) disposal
    (D) investigation
    (E) all the foregoing

92. Which of the following is the only thing which is always true concerning an evacuation of a building:
    (A) the officer responding to the call should contact the manager upon his arrival and advise the manager on the safest method of handling the bomb scare
    (B) if the manager refuses to evacuate the building, police have the authority to forcibly evacuate it
    (C) if the manager refuses to evacuate the building, the police may search for the bomb without a warrant and without his consent
    (D) occupants of the building are never in greater jeopardy when they are clearing a building than if they remained in place

93. Every bomb scare should be treated as real until:
    (A) reasonable search and investigation of the threatened location proves the message false or fails to locate a bomb
    (B) no explosions are reported within 24 hours
    (C) the subject is apprehended
    (D) none of the above

94. If the building manager is ordered to evacuate the building each time a bomb scare is had, what is likely to happen:
    (A) the manager may not call the police the next time he receives a bomb threat
    (B) if a business is forced to evacuate daily it may become bankrupt because of large financial losses from lack of business during the time of the evacuation
    (C) the occupants may become so blasé they refuse to evacuate
    (D) the best way to secure a peaceful, orderly evacuation is to call a civil defense practice or a fire drill
    (E) all the foregoing are true

95. Search of a building for a bomb can best be performed by:
    (A) the first officer at the scene
    (B) the occupants of the building
    (C) a well-trained bomb search crew in protective armor
    (D) a well-trained "bomb sniffing" dog team

96. A good public relations program will teach the owners, mana-
    gers, and occupants of all large potential bombing sites what to
    do in the event of a bomb scare. Which of the following are good
    reasons for this program:
    (A) protection of life and property
    (B) to save time in the search for the bomb
    (C) to prevent panic and loss of business
    (D) to apprehend the suspect so he will not be making any
        more calls
    (E) all the foregoing

97. Where is the most common place for a bomb:
    (A) in the bathroom
    (B) on the roof
    (C) in the foyer
    (D) outside

98. Radio transmitters may explode .... prematurely:
    (A) fuse caps and primers
    (B) dynamite
    (C) detonating cord
    (D) electric blasting caps
    (E) all of the above

99. The most common location for bombs to be found are:
    (A) outside the building
    (B) the entrance and first floor
    (C) bathrooms and storerooms
    (D) waste receptacles
    (E) all the above are among the most common places for
        bombs to be found

100. Which of the following is an incorrect statement concerning
     searches for bombs:
     (A) the custodians play a large part in searches
     (B) sometimes reports are made of bombs in order to get
         police concentrated at the location of the report so that
         other crimes may be committed elsewhere
     (C) firemen are better than police for searching for bombs
     (D) bomb squad personnel can quickly search large areas
         by themselves

101. The only positive way to be sure a bomb is not in a building is to:
   (A) demolish it completely
   (B) use X-rays
   (C) have explosive sniffing dogs completely cover the entire building
   (D) reasonable visual inspection

102. One of the following statements may be in error; which is it:
   (A) to find a bomb in ten per cent of the times when a bomb search is made is a high percentage of "finds"
   (B) after a call, when an object is found which resembles a bomb, it is often a hoax bomb
   (C) only the most obvious places can be searched for the most obvious bombs in a reasonable time
   (D) when a search is completed, the manager should be told that the area is perfectly safe and that there is no bomb

103. Of which of the following do officials generally think when searching for a bomb:
   (A) a packaged time bomb
   (B) a booby-trapped package
   (C) a booby-trap attached to a door, a locker, furniture, or windows
   (D) a movement-initiated package bomb

104. Airplane bomb scares can be handled in approximately how long, if proper procedure is followed:
   (A) 1 hour
   (B) 2 hours
   (C) 4 hours
   (D) 8 hours
   (E) 24 hours

105. Bombs are most commonly found in airplanes in the:
   (A) engine compartment
   (B) wheel well
   (C) passenger compartment or baggage hold
   (D) the fuel area and the pilot's cabin

106. The reason for having passengers search their own luggage in airplane bomb scares is:
   (A) safety
   (B) expediency
   (C) reduction of claims of theft against police
   (D) reduction of claims of breakage against police
   (E) all of the above

107. Why do bombers call police or others concerning a bomb:

  (A) to prevent innocent victims being injured, if there has been a bomb failure or misfire
  (B) to insure that police, firemen, or victims be present and injured or killed when a bomb does go off
  (C) to make sure the bomb recipient is aware that a bomb has been planted, in order to facilitate an extortion
  (D) any of the foregoing

108. A threat to bomb a location should be followed by what security measure:

  (A) search
  (B) guards
  (C) search and guards
  (D) none of the above

109. The Mad Bomber who popularized bomb scares was:

  (A) George Metesky
  (B) Ralph Emerson
  (C) Charles B. Munroe
  (D) Alfred Gatling

110. False bomb reports and bomb scares are usually communicated by which of the following:

  (A) the victim, by telephone to the police
  (B) an anonymous person, by telephone
  (C) an anonymous note or letter
  (D) by a messenger

111. What is usually the most important question to ask the anonymous bomb scare caller:

  (A) where
  (B) what
  (C) when
  (D) how
  (E) who

112. The recipient of an anonymous telephone bomb call should be questioned closely about it. Which of the following are items which should be included in the questioning:

  (A) the exact words used by the caller
  (B) background noises at the caller's end of the line
  (C) voice accent or speech impediment of the caller
  (D) opinion as to sex, age, and attitude of the caller
  (E) all the foregoing

113. Positive identification of a voice through voice print requires usually:

    (A) one word
    (B) two words
    (C) five words
    (D) ten words
    (E) none of the above

114. When a suspect bomb is found the first duty of the first officer on the scene is:

    (A) evacuate the area
    (B) determine if the item is a bomb before calling the bomb squad
    (C) set up protective barriers
    (D) turn off his radio

115. Which of the following are assisted by cooperation with the news media in a bomb disposal situation:

    (A) helps public relations
    (B) can assist in obtaining hazardous duty pay and equipment for the bomb squad
    (C) lets public know of your availability and stimulates reports of storages of explosives and of suspects
    (D) all of the foregoing

116. Which of the following is true about publicity concerning bombs and bomb threats:

    (A) the more information released, the more citizens get ideas for false reports
    (B) the more information released, the more people get the idea of using bomb threats and bombings to their own advantage
    (C) publicity leads to experimentation with explosives by children
    (D) all the foregoing

117. The first officer on the scene (fireman or policeman) should order the immediate evacuation of all persons to a place which is a safe distance from the bomb's suspected location. The minimum distance in which safety can be assumed is:

    (A) 100 feet
    (B) 200 feet
    (C) 300 feet
    (D) 500 feet
    (E) 1,000 feet

27

118. Which of the following statements is in error:

    (A)   protective barriers (walls and vehicles, etc.) will lessen the evacuation distance required, depending on the size of the bomb

    (B)   bystanders should be kept away from windows

    (C)   if the suspected item weighs less than a pound and has no fragmentation, people may be safe from serious injury in adjoining rooms

    (D)   the policeman or firefighter should place the suspected bomb or explosive against a wall so that minimum damage will be done

119. Distance and barriers may provide protection from which effects of an explosion:

    (A)   heat

    (B)   pressure

    (C)   fragmentation

    (D)   all three of the above

    (E)   none of the above

120. Of the following statements:

    1.   immediate response should be provided on any call about explosives and the bomb disposal vehicle should be taken on every call

    2.   the bomb technician should gain all possible information about the bomb before leaving the station

    (A)   both statements are true

    (B)   the first statement is true, the second is false

    (C)   the second statement is true, the first is false

    (D)   both statements are false

121. Usually what is the first question that should be asked by the bomb specialist of the officer in charge at the scene of a closed or partly closed bomb:

    (A)   why do you think it is a bomb

    (B)   where is the bomb

    (C)   has it been moved

    (D)   what is it suspected of being

    (E)   who discovered it, and when

122. What piece of equipment is the most helpful to a bomb disposal technician who must work on a suspect package bomb:

    (A)   listening device

    (B)   X-ray machine

    (C)   knife and wire cutter

    (D)   oil immersion tank

123. What should the officers or firemen at the scene be advised by the bomb specialist to do:

    (A)   "Come on with me. I need someone to help lift the bomb."
    (B)   "Keep everybody away; this may be dangerous."
    (C)   "Stand back out of danger, but be ready to give me first aid if it blows up on me."
    (D)   any of the above statements, depending on the circumstances

124. How many bomb disposal specialists should be used to approach a bomb:

    (A)   one
    (B)   two
    (C)   three
    (D)   four

125. Which of the following is the safest method of disposal of any bomb or explosive:

    (A)   freezing it, by using liquid nitrogen
    (B)   blowing it up in place
    (C)   removing firing device
    (D)   transporting bomb to remote area and detonating it there

126. Which of the following components of bombs may be deactivated by freezing:

    (A)   batteries
    (B)   mechanical delays
    (C)   corrosive delays
    (D)   explosives
    (E)   all of the above

127. The man who first propounded the remote moval of all bombs, no matter how simple they appear was:

    (A)   Doctor Muhlberger
    (B)   Monsieur Kling
    (C)   Professor Kyrsta
    (D)   Lieutenant Pike

128. The safest method of moving a suspected bomb is by:

    (A)   placing it in a bomb carrier
    (B)   using bulldozer blade to push it
    (C)   by remote control
    (D)   any of the foregoing, depending upon the circumstances

129. The safest method of dismantling electrical bomb circuits is:

    (A)   cutting with a knife
    (B)   cutting with a wire cutter
    (C)   breaking with a rope or string
    (D)   unwrapping the connections

130. A bomb is moved remotely by a bomb disposal specialist for which possible reason:

    (A)   an anti disturbance device in the bomb
    (B)   a hang fire
    (C)   a sensitive explosive
    (D)   a faulty electrical contact
    (E)   all of the above

131. Doctor Muhlberger wrote an article on how he used an X-ray machine to dismantle a bomb in:

    (A)   1937
    (B)   1947
    (C)   1957
    (D)   1967

132. Which material best provides protection from X-ray for the operator:

    (A)   glass
    (B)   cement
    (C)   lead
    (D)   steel
    (E)   wood

133. Fluoroscopy is very helpful in determining whether or not an item is a bomb. Whenever fluoroscopy cannot be used because of the size of the item, or light conditions, etc., X-ray photographs should be taken for which of the following reasons:

    (A)   the picture provides a permanent record in the event the item explodes
    (B)   time spent near a bomb fluoroscoping it may be shortened since the film may be developed and studied at a safe distance
    (C)   radiation exposure for the technician is less
    (D)   a television camera has been developed to use with the X-ray machine so that the operator will not be in danger if the bomb has been rigged to explode by X-ray
    (E)   all of the above are valid reasons

134. All of the effects of X-ray on the body will dissipate in:
   (A) 6 hours
   (B) 1 day
   (C) 4 days
   (D) none of the above

135. An enclosed bomb can be opened remotely by three methods. Which of the following is not one of these methods:
   (A) bomb tongs
   (B) projectiles
   (C) rope loops, one tied to stationary object, other to moving truck
   (D) explosives

136. The best method of disposing of suspected closed bombs is:
   (A) blow it up in place
   (B) freeze it
   (C) burn it
   (D) opening it remotely
   (E) the method used will vary with the circumstances

137. The best method of opening bombs remotely is:
   (A) the water cannon
   (B) gun fire
   (C) tongs
   (D) explosives

138. Which of the following is a disadvantage to dismantling bombs remotely with a protective shield and long extended poles fitted with tools:
   (A) distance from possible explosion
   (B) greater safety
   (C) limited visibility and control
   (D) all the foregoing are disadvantages

139. The effects of an explosion are:
   (A) pressure
   (B) heat
   (C) fragmentation
   (D) all three

140. How many kinds of protection do we have against bombs?
   (A) one
   (B) two
   (C) three
   (D) protection is unlimited

141. Which of the following is the recommended safest approach to bomb disposal if the bomb must be moved to dispose of it:

(A) place the bomb in an envelope and have it carried on poles on the shoulders of men wearing bomb suits

(B) use devices to remotely place bomb into bomb carrier on a vehicle

(C) drag bomb in a basket to an area safe for its disposal

(D) any of the above are perfectly safe methods of bomb disposal

142. Bomb blankets provide protection on:

(A) pipe bombs

(B) grenades

(C) incendiary devices

(D) all three

143. What effect does explosion pressure have on the human body:

(A) disintegration

(B) bursting of liquid filled parts

(C) ear damage

(D) lung damage

(E) all of the above

144. When storing explosives protection should be provided for:

(A) safety

(B) security

(C) both of the above

(D) none of the above

145. There are four most common types of body armor; which of the following is not one of them:

(A) molded ceramic

(B) ballistic nylon

(C) sheet lead

(D) fiber glass in soft layers

(E) steel

146. How many magazines should be provided for storage of evidence explosives:

(A) one

(B) two

(C) four

(D) one for each investigative case

(E) two for each investigative case

147. Which explosive is not stable when old and should be exploded:

   (A)   C4
   (B)   black powder
   (C)   detonating cord
   (D)   dynamite

148. The most penetrating type of explosive charge is called the:

   (A)   Monroe effect
   (B)   cavity charge
   (C)   shaped charge
   (D)   all of the above

149. When objects must be, for safety's sake or other reasons, detonated before being presented in court as evidence, which of the following should be done in order to prove that an explosion took place and what type of explosion it was:

   (A)   photograph all explosions
   (B)   photograph all craters
   (C)   photograph all explosions and all craters both in color and in black and white
   (D)   measure and describe all objects both before disposal or after, as the safest case may be

150. For disposal of bombs by the blasting procedure, how many men are there on the blasting team:

   (A)   one
   (B)   two
   (C)   three
   (D)   four

ANSWERS

1. (C) If the police officer investigates a suspected bomb too closely he may kill himself and others. Call for the bomb squad. P. 3

2. (E) Booby trap wires and other initiating systems may be found in any location with the explosive. P. 3

3. (C) Too often, police and fire agencies will wait until a bomb is found before any decision is made to initiate precautionary measures for the future. P. 3

4. (A) Planning in advance for emergencies and other special situations. Don't wait until you have a bomb before deciding what to do with it. P. 4

5. (E) Don't be misguided and overcompensate because of one incident or for political reasons in planning for future incidents. p. 4

6. (E) The first element of a tactical plan for bomb incident control is to determine who is going to be responsible for disposal of a bomb if one is found. P. 4

7. (A) The more experience a bomb specialist has, the safer he is. P. 4

8. (B) If future bomb incident needs are minimal, small departments may be better off if they consider nearby outside assistance, or pooled information and equipment with other small departments. P. 4

9. (E) The bomb disposal specialist's opinion should be respected by his superior officer and the superior officer bears the responsiblity of his men's actions. P. 5

10. (D) Any of these groups, or all of them, will take unnecessary chances with bombs. P. 5

11. (C) Bomb disposal, even though some police and law enforcement agencies believe that it is, is NOT ordinarily a function of the FBI. Pp. 5,6

12. (C) Their other duties may prevent EOD personnel from a certain base from responding to requests from local police. P. 6

13. (A) The facilities of the U. S. Secret Service are for the protection of the President and Vice President. Help from local Air Force and Navy bases depends upon the policy of the EOD detachment or their base commanders. P. 6

14. (E) All the listed items are limitations and problems connected with assistance by the Armed Services in bomb investigations Pp. 6,7

15. (D) The Institute is a self regulating body for the explosives manufacturing industry and provides dummy explosive samples for a small fee. P. 7

16. (B) The safest method, the most practical and the most complete school of bomb disposal is at Redstone Arsenal, Alabama. P. 8

17. (B) Due to a recent change in policy, these schools will cover only military ordnance, and not explosives and bombs in general. P. 8

18. (B) Before the Justice Department established the National Bomb Data Center there wasn't much literature available on bomb disposal. P. 10

19. (E) When organizing a bomb squad police administrators should take all of the above into consideration. Getting the job done in the safest method possible is the main consideration. P. 11

20. (C) A one-man bomb squad is not adequate, since the man may be out of town on vacation, on business, or at school. P. 11

21. (D) Only an inexperienced person would believe that all bombs can be deactivated. P. 12

22. (C) New York City developed the first bomb carrier by testing. P. 13

23. (B) The most simple approach for a novice bomb technician is to use a remote-control device to place the bomb in a carrier, and remove it to a safe place to work on it. P. 12

24. (B) There are three basic types of bomb carriers which have been developed. P. 12

25. (A) The Dade County Public Safety Department in 1971, and don't let anyone tell you differently. Over 200 copies have been made since then but now this design may be made obsolete by a complete confinement sphere. P. 14

26. (E) These are all primary considerations. Add in other factors, such as bulkiness, cost, ease of fabrication, etc. Pp. 13-20

27. (A) The time of an explosion is between 3 milliseconds for C4 and 100 milliseconds for black powder. P. 15

28. (D) An explosion goes in all directions like a sunburst and will travel the path of least resistance. If a barrier is too strong for the force of the explosion it wall cause the force to be reflected. P. 18

29. (A) The truck is usually easier to drive than a trailer. P. 20

30. (A) Reports are highly inaccurate. P. 20

31. (C) Whenever a bomb call is received, the bomb carrier should be taken along. P. 20

32. (B) Anyone who has worked on a number of bombs will tell you they find these are the most commonly used tools. P. 22

33. (A) Both statements are true. Pp. 22-28

34. (C) Shunted electric blasting caps can be carried and are not affected by a radio. P. 23

35. (C) The X-ray machine is the most expensive but sometimes the most essential tool. P. 24

36. (A) These chemicals will desensitize nitroglycerine. P. 24

37. (A) A steam explosion is a form of mechanical explosion. P. 30

38. (E) Implosion is described graphically with illustrations. Pp. 30,31

39. (E) All of these are explosions according to the text. P. 30

40. (A) There are three types of explosions, as named in the foreword of the question. P. 30

41. (A)   Mechanical explosions often do not make loud reports. P. 30

42. (D)   is not part of the triangle; the explosion is initiated by heat, but must contain fuel and oxygen — in the case of an explosion the fuel being supplied usually by carbon and the oxygen by an item such as potassium chlorate.   P. 32

43. (E)   A fire is much slower than an explosion; an explosion must contain its own oxygen; and in the production of an explosive, fuel must be mixed with oxygen.   P. 32

44. (C)   Chemicals explode from 3 milliseconds to 100 milliseconds. 100 milliseconds are a tenth of a second.   P. 32

45. (B)   This is the only statement that is true. There are a lot of dead people who thought the other answers were correct.   P. 32

46. (A)   That's all it takes besides careful temperature control. P. 32

47. (E)   All of these are different explosives.   Pp. 32,33

48. (C)   This explosive can explode all by itself at any time during or after mixing.   P. 33

49. (A)   All explosives slower than 16,000 feet per second display this characteristic.   P. 33

50. (A)   This is why pipe bombs are common. The other answers are advantages but usually are not the main reason for placing the powder in pipes.   P. 33

51. (E)   All the statements are correct.   Pp. 32-34

52. (B)   There are two types of blasting caps: electric and fuse. P. 34

53. (A)   This is the best of the definitions. B is wrong — it is not always necessary to deliver with an unlawful intent. C is an old expression for a bomb with a complex mechanism. D is not always true — the explosive need not be in a container.   P.34

54. (E)   The venturi is the opening in the rear of a rocket motor through which the heat and pressure escape causing the propulsion of the rocket in the opposite direction.   P. 34

55. (C)   A bomb may be delivered (planted or set) by being placed, dropped, thrown, or projected.   J. 34

56. (D)   A limpit mine is an explosive charge that is attached with adhesive tape, magnets, or chain to a target such as ships or fuel-storage tanks.   Pp. 34,35

57. (D)   The bomber is on the offense and your protective measures are all defense.   P. 35

58. (A)   An "open bomb" is one in which the means of initiation and explosive can be seen, and a "closed bomb" is one in which the component parts are covered in a container.   P. 35

59. (C)   An innocent person such as a child may either be near the bomb when it explodes or may explode a booby-trap bomb.   P. 35

60. (D) Bombs have three methods of being initiated: timed control, motion, and remote control. P. 35

61. (A) The time bomb is the most common bomb found in the United States. Pp. 35,36

62. (C) A battery holding an electrical relay open until the battery dies and the relay falls to complete a second circuit containing another battery and an electric blasting cap. P. 36

63. (C) Remote control is not one of the four general types of time delays, which are: burning, corrosive, electrical, and mechanical. P. 36

64. (B) The more United States troops walking around in Viet Nam, the more were injured by booby traps. This is the first time for this large a percentage of casualties. P. 36

65. (A) Burning black powder fuse is the most common type of delay. P. 36

66. (C) The motion type of initiation is often used in booby-trap bombs; package bombs are just portable booby traps. P. 37

67. (D) The reader who thinks about it should be able to derive this information from the text. Pp. 37,38

68. (E) The anti-disturbance devices are primarily of four functions: pull, tension release, pressure, and pressure release. P. 38

69. (A) The remote control method of initiation is usually one of these three: electronic, electrical, and mechanical. P. 38

70. (D) A Molotov cocktail does not explode; even an incendiary device that is made of hypergolic chemicals that burn upon mixing cannot be termed a bomb. Pp. 39-41

71. (A) A Molotov cocktail is an incendiary which is a flammable device designed to burn in a specific manner. P. 39

72. (B) Hypergolic chemicals make the most unstable and dangerous bombs to handle. P. 41

73. (D) This is all that an expert is. P. 41,42

74. (C) Those who work with bombs are termed "bomb technicians" or "bomb specialists" until the Court decides whether the witness is qualified through his experience and knowledge to be called an expert and able to render an opinion on bomb matters. P. 41

75. (D) Bombers obtain their explosives by buying, stealing, or making them; tight control of explosives makes it difficult to buy them or steal them; making them is relatively simple, because such powerful explosives can be made from readily-available materials. P. 43

76. (C) The caption under Figure 37 clearly indicates to the wise that burning dynamite may explode so evacuation is the correct procedure. P. 44

77. (B) Earth moving for quarries, road building and tunnels help progress. P. 45

78. (C)   Lax laws on explosives may cause disasters which may result in over enthusiasm in passing legislation that hurts the explosives industry thus hurting the economy and welfare of modern civilization. Pp. 43,44,45

79. (A)   When legislators pass new laws they seldom provide additional personnel to make the laws enforceable.   P. 46

80. (A)   Powder monkeys are also known as powder men who move and carry and load the explosives, etc.   P. 46

81. (B)   The photographs on page 47 are good examples to show the victim was facing the explosion.   P. 47

82. (C)   Because of the potential of other violent crimes police should realize that every possible effort should be made to recover the explosives.   P. 48

83. (C)   In most areas of the country, 90% of dynamite thefts result in bombings.   P. 48

84. (B)   Although the manufacturers take extreme precautions in quality control and warn blasters never to use less than two feet of fuse, blasters who want to save time or money cut their fuse shorter which too often results in cutting their lives too short.   P. 48

85. (D)   All of these motives are illustrated in the text.   P. 49

86. (D)   All of these statements are false. Amount, position, and type of explosive can all vary the effects of an explosion.   P. 50

87. (A)   This has resulted in several deaths.   P. 51

88. (B)   Settling of structures causes linear or vertical cracks and settling can be expedited by vibrations.   P. 52

89. (C)   All such reports are investigated and handled by the Federal Bureau of Investigation.   P. 53

90. (C)   The McClellan Committee hearings resulted in additional federal assistance through the National Bomb Data Center, the Hazardous Devices School and additional regulation of interstate shipment of explosives and bombing laws.   P. 53

91. (E)   Items A through D are all items of extreme importance in preparation of any tactical plan concerning bomb scares.   P. 54

92. (A)   This is the only thing which is always true; there is no constitutional law that gives police the right to forcibly evacuate the bulding or to conduct a search without a warrant; if the bomb happens to be near one of the exits of the building, occupants may be placed in greater jeopardy as they leave than if they stayed where they were. Pp. 54,55

93. (A)   Every report of a bomb should be treated as the real thing. P. 54

94. (E)   These are all true statements.   P. 55

95. (B)   Searching a location for a bomb is best performed by occupants of the building; they know the location and can tell immediately that no unusual objects are in their particular area.   P. 55

96. (E)   These are all good reasons for the program.   P. 55

97. (D)　Most bombs are found or exploded outside buildings because of easy access.　P. 55

98. (D)　These are the only explosives which may be exploded by radio transmissions.　P. 56

99. (E)　This is the listing of most common places for bombs; found on pp. 56 and 57.

100. (D)　Bomb squad personnel cannot quickly search large areas by themselves, but they should stand by for technical advice or until a suspected bomb is found.　P. 57

101. (A)　Bombs can be concealed within walls, floors or ceilings and the only certain method of determining a bomb is not in the building is by demolishing it completely.　P. 57

102. (D)　NEVER tell a manager or complainant that an area is perfectly safe or that there is no bomb. Instead, they should be told that a **bomb was not found.**　P. 57

103. (A)　Officials think in terms of a packaged time bomb when they are searching.　P. 58

104. (A)　Airplane bomb scares can be handled in approximately one hour.　P. 58

105. (C)　Almost all airplane bombs have been in these two areas. P. 58

106. (E)　All of these statements are true.　P. 58,59

107. (D)　All three reasons are advanced in the text.　Pp. 59-61

108. (C)　A threat may follow a bomb already at the location but usually means future action.　P. 60

109. (A)　Metesky started more social ills than he realized.　P. 61

110. (B)　Usually such false bomb reports and bomb threats are communicated by telephone by an anonymous person.　P. 61

111. (A)　Trying to find the bomb is usually the whole time consuming problem.　P. 62

112. (E)　All these items are mentioned as being of importance in questioning the recipient of an anonymous telephone bomb call.　P.63

113. (D)　Ten words are usually sufficient for a positive identification of a voice.　P. 63

114. (A)　The protection of life is the paramount consideration. P. 64

115. (D)　These are the main advantages of cooperation with the news media.　P. 64

116. (D)　These are the main disadvantages of publicity about bombs and bomb threats.　P. 64

117. (C)　In determining the extent of evacuation required, it shall be assumed that a bomb or explosive may cause damage and fatal or serious injury to persons within an area of at least 300 feet from the point of explosion.　P. 64

118. (D)　The policeman or firefighter should UNDER NO CIRCUMSTANCES TOUCH A SUSPECTED BOMB OR EXPLOSIVE.　P. 65

119. (D)   Depending upon the size and type of explosive, size and type of fragmentation and the thickness and type of barriers.   P. 65

120. (B)   The bomb technician should not waste time obtaining information on the telephone that can better be obtained at the scene, especially if the suspect item appears to be a time bomb, because every second may count.   Pp. 65,66

121. (A)   The first question to be asked is "Why do you think it is a bomb?"   P. 66

122. (B)   An X-ray machine sometimes takes the surprise out of a suspected closed bomb.   P. 66

123. (C)   Before approaching the bomb, the technician should advise officers or firemen at the scene to stand back and to apply first aid if needed.   P. 67

124. (A)   It is usually an unnecessary risk to use more than one man near a bomb.   P. 67

125. (B)   The safest method of disposal of any bomb or explosive is to blow it up in place by setting another charge on it.   P. 67

126. (E)   All of these although some explosives require the most extensive freezing.   P. 68

127. (A)   Doctor Muhlberger wrote an article on this in 1937.   P. 69

128. (C)   Moving a suspected bomb by remote control is one of the safest methods.   P. 69

129. (C)   The safest method of working on bombs is often the remote methods.   P. 70

130. (E)   Any of the above may cause a bomb to explode.   P. 71

131. (A)   1937   P. 72

132. (C)   The heavy density of lead prevents penetration of X-ray. P. 73

133. (E)   These reasons, and more, are listed in the text.   P. 74

134. (D)   Radioactivity is absorbed by the human body and leaves very slowly. The effects are accumulative.   P. 74

135. (C)   Rope loops can almost never be used; they are used to move the bomb from remote location. The other three methods are most generally used to open bombs.   P. 74

136. (E)   Every suspect bomb and situation is different.   P. 75

137. (A)   The military shotgun dearmer is filled with water instead of a steel slug.   P. 76 second printing

138. (C)   Disadvantages are limited visibility and control in critical work and the time spent in setting up the shield.   P. 77

139. (D)   The bomb disposal specialist may be injured or killed by any of these effects.   P. 77

140. (B)   Distance and barriers   P. 78

141. (B)   Use of remote control devices to place a bomb into a bomb carrier on a vehicle is one of the safest approaches if the bomb technician lacks knowledge and proficiency in dismantling bombs. P. 78

142. (D)   A bomb blanket is especially effective on these items depending on their size.   P. 79

143. (E)   Bomb disposal specialists may suffer any or all of the above injuries in the line of duty.   P. 80

144. (C)   Distance from inhabited buildings, locks and watchmen are preventive measures.   P. 81

145. (C)   Sheet lead is not used because of its weight and relatively easy penetrability.   P. 80

146. (B)   Two magazines should be provided, one for blasting caps and firing devices and one for bulk explosives.   P. 81

147. (D)   Old dynamite is often unstable but the other explosives are usually stable when old.   P. 82

148. (D)   These are all names for the same type of charge.   P. 83

149. (D)   All objects in question should be photographed both in black and white and in color, measured and described as to color and markings before disposal or after, as the safest case may be.   P. 84

150. (B)   All blasting must be performed by at least two persons; two is the usual number on the team.   P. 86

42

1. When exploding a suspected bomb with another explosive the best place to set the explosive is:
   (A) on the top
   (B) under the bomb
   (C) on the side away from the disposal technician
   (D) on the side closest to the disposal technician

2. Which of the following is necessary for a conviction on possession of explosives:
   (A) bring the explosives into court to be presented as an exhibit
   (B) exploding a sample of the explosive and testifying to the fact that it exploded
   (C) chemical analysis and exploding some of the explosive
   (D) explode some and bring the rest to court

3. The safety warning before the blaster sets off a charge is:
   (A) Duck
   (B) Take cover
   (C) Ready
   (D) Fire in the hole

4. Freezing a bomb to deactivate it is called:
   (A) cryogenics
   (B) cooling it
   (C) icing down
   (D) frosting

5. Which is the correct order of arrangement in fluoroscoping with the X-ray machine:
   (A) X-ray, bomb, fluoroscope, operator
   (B) bomb, fluoroscope, X-ray, operator
   (C) operator, X-ray, fluoroscope, bomb
   (D) X-ray, fluoroscope, operator, bomb
   (E) X-ray, operator, fluoroscope, bomb

6. Which is proper storage of recovered explosives and bombs:
   (A) one magazine for all explosives and bombs
   (B) one magazine for blasting caps and bulk explosives and one for triggering devices
   (C) one magazine for caps and triggering devices and one for bulk explosives
   (D) one magazine for bulk explosives and triggering devices and one magazine for blasting caps

7. The manufacturers of safety fuse state that the minimum length of safety fuse for safe use is:

   (A) one foot
   (B) two feet
   (C) three feet
   (D) four feet
   (E) five feet

8. Usually, two bomb technicians operate together. Upon arriving at the scene of a reported bomb in a vehicle, the first technician should carry a flashlight with him as he approaches the vehicle. Which of the following should the second technician do:

   (A) wait for instructions from the first technician
   (B) photograph the vehicle from a safe distance, taking photographs which show both sides, front, rear, license tag, and location of the vehicle
   (C) get all equipment out of bomb disposal vehicle and arrange it so that he can pass it to the first technician upon request
   (D) back the bomb disposal trailer up to the suspect vehicle so that the bomb can be loaded quickly and efficiently

9. Where is the most common place bombs are found in cars:

   (A) under the seat
   (B) under the gas tank
   (C) attached to the right rear door
   (D) under the hood, on the left side of the engine against the firewall, hooked to the ignition

10. When examining a vehicle for a bomb the first thing the first bomb technician should do is:

   (A) walk directly to the vehicle and look inside, through the windows, at both the front and rear seat areas, of both sides
   (B) walk around the vehicle and make a general observation without touching it
   (C) go directly to the vehicle, lie down on his back, and using his flashlight, look up into the motor compartment for a bomb, explosive, wire, fuse, or anything unusual about the vehicle
   (D) open the right front door and look up behind the dash to see if there is any bomb concealed there

11. Bombs that won't explode are sometimes left by the bomber for what reason:

   (A) practice
   (B) extortion
   (C) practical jokes
   (D) none of the above

12. How can you tell if a bomb was placed on the inside or the outside of a gasoline tank:

   (A) torn edges of the hole in the metal caused by the explosion are bent inward
   (B) torn edges of the metal are bent outward by implosion
   (C) fingerprints on the outside
   (D) fire

13. Fragments from a car bombing can travel as far as:

   (A) 300 feet
   (B) 400 feet
   (C) 500 feet
   (D) 600 feet

14. What type of initiating system for a bomb might be expected to be found when opening cars:

   (A) pressure
   (B) pressure release
   (C) tension
   (D) tension release
   (E) all of the above

15. How may the hood of the automobile be raised by remote control:

   (A) by ropes
   (B) by levers
   (C) by fulcrums
   (D) by use of all three

16. Which is the least commonly used door on an automobile, if it has four doors:

   (A) the right front
   (B) the left front
   (C) the right rear
   (D) the left rear

45

17. What is usually the best method of removing bombs from cars:
    (A) before moving the bomb place a bomb blanket over it
    (B) slide your fingers under the bomb feeling for other initiating systems
    (C) disconnect the car battery
    (D) no matter how simple the bomb appears move it remotely first

18. Where might a bomb be found:
    (A) under the tires
    (B) in or on the exhaust system
    (C) in or on the gas tank
    (D) under the driver's seat
    (E) all of the above

19. What is the only way you can positively feel there is no bomb in a car:
    (A) completely dismantle and open every part of the car
    (B) a thorough reasonable search
    (C) running an electric current through the car
    (D) driving the car
    (E) none of the above

20. When receiving a bomb call who can you rely upon to tell you if an item is an explosive or bomb and what type:
    (A) the complainant
    (B) the police officer
    (C) the complaint desk
    (D) the dispatcher
    (E) none of the above

21. Of the following statements, which is correct:
    (A) persons finding bombs seldom move them
    (B) the bomb technician should carefully examine the item before moving it remotely or touching it
    (C) bombs never explode from movement of items around them
    (D) anything believed to be so sensitive to initiation that it may explode upon being moved should be disposed of as soon as possible; don't take time to photograph it

22. What is the best thing to do if a police officer not on the bomb squad handles suspected explosives or bombs:
    (A) give him a medal
    (B) suspend him
    (C) give him additional bomb training
    (D) none of the above

23. To identify an explosive, the technician should:

    (A) cut a small piece off, and take it to a safe place and hit it with a hammer
    (B) pour sulphuric acid over it; the smoke will be a dark brown
    (C) cut off a small piece, place it on a piece of paper, then set fire to it; an explosive will flare up, torch, or sparkle
    (D) try to set fire to a small piece of the object; if it does not burn, it is not an explosive

24. Which two chemicals will explode if mixed:

    (A) Score hair cream and ammonia
    (B) red phosphorus and potassium chlorate
    (C) nitric acid and sulfuric acid
    (D) gasoline and sulfuric acid
    (E) none of the above

25. A hypergolic mixture is:

    (A) a mixture of sodium hyperchlorite and water
    (B) two substances that ignite upon being mixed together
    (C) a mixture of alcohol and hydrochloric acid
    (D) two substances that may explode upon being mixed together
    (E) a fuel for piston-type race cars

26. "Violent reaction" as stated by chemical companies means:

    (A) explosion
    (B) ignition
    (C) bubbling and foaming
    (D) none of the above

27. Which of the following will explode upon contact with water:

    (A) sodium
    (B) phosphorus
    (C) potassium nitrate
    (D) thermite

28. How many kinds of phosphorus are there:

    (A) one
    (B) two
    (C) three
    (D) four

47

29. Explosives are recovered by the authorities in mining towns in which circumstances:

   (A)   stolen explosives
   (B)   discarded explosives
   (C)   illegal explosives
   (D)   abandoned explosives
   (E)   all of the above

30. When discarded, stolen, or illegal explosives or explosives from bombs are found, what of the following should be included in a report on the incident:

   (A)   type, size, and color of explosive
   (B)   approximate weight
   (C)   labels, batch number, and manufacturer
   (D)   exact count of items
   (E)   all the foregoing

31. If you recover dynamite which is the most likely item to be recovered also:

   (A)   prima cord
   (B)   caps
   (C)   fuse
   (D)   TNT

32. Information which may be obtained from blasting caps is which of the following:

   (A)   length of cap
   (B)   color and diameter of cap
   (C)   type of crimp at the top of the cap
   (D)   whether it has a round or dimpled bottom, and the type and color of the plug
   (E)   all of the foregoing, and more

33. The first place where individual sticks of dynamite had lot numbers was:

   (A)   New York City
   (B)   England
   (C)   France
   (D)   Germany

34. Which of the following is the best method of determining if a piece of cord is safety fuse or detonating cord:
    (A) detonating cord is always red in color
    (B) the safety fuse is always black in color
    (C) orange and white fuses are always detonating cord
    (D) if the core of the fuse is white, it is detonating cord; if the core of the fuse is black, it is safety fuse
    (E) if the core of the fuse is black, it is detonating cord; if the core of the fuse is white, it is safety fuse

35. Who makes most of the safety fuse in the United States:
    (A) DuPont
    (B) Kinetics Corporation
    (C) Austin
    (D) Ensign Bickford
    (E) none of the above

36. What is the maximum time delay from a roll of fuse plus or minus 10%:
    (A) 10 minutes
    (B) 25 minutes
    (C) 33 minutes
    (D) 45 minutes

37. The best reference collection on fuse and blasting caps belongs to:
    (A) the Institute of the Makers of Explosives
    (B) the Delaware State Police
    (C) Redstone Arsenal
    (D) Federal Bureau of Investigation

38. The insulation on detonating cord is found in which color or colors:
    (A) red
    (B) red and white
    (C) yellow and orange
    (D) all colors

39. If two craters are found at a bombing scene and witnesses report hearing only one explosion what type of evidence should this indicate:
    (A) electric cap wires
    (B) fuse
    (C) wrappers from ditching dynamite
    (D) a clock timer
    (E) none of the above

49

40. Which statement is not true:

   (A) Like lightning, bombers don't strike twice at the same place
   (B) Bombers do repeat
   (C) There may be more than one bomb at the scene of a bombing
   (D) Two bombers may attack the same target

41. Detonating cord explosions sometimes leave what type of evidence:

   (A) pieces of detonating cord blown off where it was tied together
   (B) pieces of the fusing system of the bomb
   (C) pressure and burn marks
   (D) all of the above

42. If all of the evidence is destroyed by the bomb what kind of case might be used on the bomber when his house is searched:

   (A) nothing, all the evidence was destroyed
   (B) bombing
   (C) placing or throwing a deadly missile
   (D) possession of explosives without a permit

43. According to the Interstate Commerce Commission dynamite cartridges and boxes must be marked:

   (A) DYNAMITE
   (B) EXPLOSIVES
   (C) DO NOT BURN
   (D) with all of the ingredients so you will know exactly how to destroy it

44. How is dynamite always packaged:

   (A) in fifty-pound cases
   (B) in large cylindrical cartridges, with the diameter and weight stamped on them
   (C) in bulk barrels, resembling sawdust
   (D) in all the foregoing
   (E) as in A and B, but not C

45. When dynamite is covered with moisture or oozing moisture then:

   (A) the dynamite is liable to explode if you touch it
   (B) the dynamite won't explode at all
   (C) the moisture is pure nitroglycerine
   (D) the moisture is pure water
   (E) the moisture is usually water with no nitroglycerine

46. What happens to dynamite when it is improperly stored, for instance, in high heat and humidity:
    (A) it attracts moisture and is ruined rapidly
    (B) the water and oxidizing salts dry out, leaving a very unstable mixture of nitro carbo nitrate and nitroglycerine
    (C) the outside of the dynamite stick becomes oily
    (D) all the foregoing
    (E) A and B, but not C

47. When dynamite gets old it becomes:
    (A) softer
    (B) harder
    (C) varies according to the type of dynamite and the environment
    (D) stays the same

48. Exact reproduction of bombs may disclose the:
    (A) quantity of explosives
    (B) initiating system
    (C) source of bomb parts
    (D) the suspect
    (E) all of the above

49. What is dynamite without nitroglycerine called:
    (A) nitro carbo nitrate
    (B) a blasting agent
    (C) an oxidizer
    (D) all the foregoing

50. Proper formulas for diesel fuel and ammonium nitrate mixtures is:
    (A) 25% diesel fuel to 75% ammonium nitrate
    (B) 75% diesel fuel to 25% ammonium nitrate
    (C) 50% diesel fuel to 50% ammonium nitrate
    (D) 6% diesel fuel to 94% ammonium nitrate

51. In order to explode nitro carbo nitrate you usually need a:
    (A) blasting cap and a booster
    (B) an electric cap and confinement
    (C) a blasting cap, a booster and confinement
    (D) a booster and a fuse cap

52. What is one thing which is true of all known boosters or primers:
    (A) they are flat discs
    (B) they are cubes
    (C) they are cylinders and have a hole in the center
    (D) they have cord sticking out of them

51

53. When TNT and RDX are combined they form:

    (A)   Composition A
    (B)   Composition B
    (C)   Composition C
    (D)   pentolite

54. Which of the following is true concerning nitroglycerine:

    (A)   it is rarely used as an explosive separately
    (B)   it is not sold by explosives companies
    (C)   the only time it is encountered is when someone has made
          it himself or extracted it from dynamite
    (D)   all the foregoing

55. The book Bombs and Bombings advises that nitroglycerine can
    be obtained:

    (A)   by cooking dynamite in water
    (B)   soaking dynamite in acetone
    (C)   mixing glycerine, nitric acid and sulfuric acid
    (D)   none of the above

56. The type of bomb used to blow a penetrating hole in steel is
    called:

    (A)   a penetrator
    (B)   fragmentation
    (C)   shaped
    (D)   steel plumb

57. Which of the following is not an identifying characteristic of
    nitroglycerine:

    (A)   it is an oil
    (B)   when the fingers touch it and are rubbed together, they
          will be slippery
    (C)   it is very salty to the taste
    (D)   its color may vary from clear or slightly yellow to
          completely maroon in color, depending upon its age

58. The antidote for a nitroglycerine headache is:

    (A)   aspirin
    (B)   caffeine
    (C)   alcohol
    (D)   milk

59. 1. To test whether or not a substance is nitroglycerine, a drop of it may be burned on a piece of paper.
2. Disposal of nitroglycerine may be accomplished wth a solution of nitroglycerine desensitizer or sawdust.
3. A desensitizer solution for nitroglycerine consists of two liquid solutions.
4. One always pours the desensitizer into the nitroglycerine, never pouring the nitroglycerine into a desensitizer.
5. When sawdust is used, the technician actually makes dynamite.
6. Washing down a safe or bank vault door which has been loaded with nitroglycerine is a relatively simple job.
Of the foregoing statements:
   (A) all are correct
   (B) 4 and 6 are incorrect
   (C) 2 and 3 are incorrect
   (D) only 1 is incorrect
   (E) all statements are incorrect

60. What hazard is encountered in washing down a safe full of nitroglycerine:
   (A) get every drop out
   (B) the solution eats the skin from your hands
   (C) disagreeable odor
   (D) all of the above

61. Which explosive has the lowest detonation velocity:
   (A) dynamite
   (B) astrolite
   (C) C4
   (D) nitroglycerine

62. Which is not a disadvantage of explosives as a method of safe burglary:
   (A) noise
   (B) danger
   (C) speed
   (D) none of the above

63. What is the name of a new explosive developed through rocket research, which is liquid and sold in two separate plastic bottles, the contents of which are not explosive until they are mixed:
   (A) DL 76
   (B) Dolomite
   (C) Astrolite
   (D) Composition C-5
   (E) Moon-power

53

64. What are kinetic explosives:
   (A) explosives that consist of two separate materials, neither of which is explosive by itself, but mixed together they form an explosive mixture and can be shipped by commercial transportation
   (B) a high energy, slow burning explosive
   (C) any explosive that a #6 blasting cap will detonate
   (D) explosives that, when detonated, throw solid particles to great distances

65. As far as military ordnance is concerned, the abbreviation RSP means:
   (A) refer to shore patrol
   (B) radiation, shock, and power
   (C) render safe procedure
   (D) none of the foregoing

66. Of the following, one statement may be in error; which one is it:
   (A) a bomber may cause a bomb incident because of anger at no specific event
   (B) the victim, if he survives, will tell the authorities the reason for a bombing, if he knows why it was done
   (C) A background check and skillful interview of the victim may bring out many reasons for the bombing
   (D) there are many bomb scares, bomb hoaxes, and small bombs exploded without the intention of causing injury or death
   (E) often a victim will not talk because of the possibility of further retaliation against him or his family

67. Which color means practice United States military ordnance:
   (A) blue
   (B) olive drab
   (C) gray
   (D) yellow

68. What is the best way to identify military ordnance:
   (A) find out from an ex-serviceman
   (B) open it up
   (C) ask the OD at the closest military base
   (D) contact the EOD unit

69. What is the preferred method of testing a hand grenade for court:
   (A) open it up
   (B) tape the grenade to a post, pull the pin with a string
   (C) pull the pin and throw it
   (D) place a charge on it

70. Which item would be most necessary to place in a photograph of an explosive:

    (A) a piece of paper bearing the case number
    (B) a piece of paper bearing the date and time
    (C) a piece of paper bearing your name or initials
    (D) a ruler

71. Package bombs are usually made:

    (A) as booby traps to cause death or injury
    (B) as time bombs
    (C) property destruction
    (D) none of the above

72. Why would an extortion bomber deliberately leave a bomb that will not explode:

    (A) He changed his mind.
    (B) Someone surprised him before he could initiate it
    (C) If the bomber kills his victim then the victim can't pay off.
    (D) None of the above.

73. Select the surest method of preventing bombings:

    (A) control the use of explosives
    (B) surveillance of suspects
    (C) arrest and conviction and imprisonment of bombers
    (D) none of the above

74. A bomb may be preceded by:

    (A) anonymous calls
    (B) stink bombs
    (C) fake bombs
    (D) a bomb
    (E) all of the above

75. Which of the following is not true:

    (A) the victim is never a possible suspect
    (B) the family, friends, and associates of the victim are always possible suspects
    (C) the majority of bombing cases which are solved are solved through evidence given by informants
    (D) the success of one bomber may cause others to get the idea and start other bombings

76. Most bombings are solved through:

    (A) anonymous calls
    (B) fingerprints
    (C) informants
    (D) evidence at the scene
    (E) confessions

77. When searching a bomb scene first:

    (A) look for another bomb
    (B) take photographs
    (C) look for damage
    (D) find the crater

78. What is the quickest way of determining what type of explosive caused an explosion:

    (A) examination of residue, if explosive fails to explode fully
    (B) photospectrographic examination of soil against which explosive was placed
    (C) sniffing the particular odor of the explosive
    (D) questioning witnesses

79. What is the most frequent reason for misfires with fuse caps:

    (A) failure to ignite the fuse
    (B) faulty crimp of the cap to the fuse
    (C) melting of the asphalt insulation, cutting off powder train
    (D) kinked fuse

80. What is the main reason for misfires with electric caps:

    (A) broken wires
    (B) improper wiring connections
    (C) dead batteries
    (D) insufficient power in the blasting cap
    (E) either B or C, but not A or D

81. The main reason for misfire with safety fuse and fuse caps is:

    (A) bending the fuse
    (B) wet fuse
    (C) fuse cutting itself off
    (D) faulty crimp

82. Gasoline explodes at what percentage to air:

    (A) 4% gasoline to 96% air
    (B) 96% gasoline to 4% air
    (C) 50% gasoline to 50% air
    (D) 75% gasoline to 25% air
    (E) 25% gasoline to 75% air

83. Gas explosions are inconsistent in effects and propagation of the explosive wave. What is the reason for this:

   (A) dryness in the atmosphere
   (B) ultraviolet light causing improper mixtures of gas vapors with air
   (C) gas vapors collecting in different areas due to air currents and confinement in structures
   (D) they are high-velocity explosions, tending to be shunted into the air due to ground configuration

84. When a victim is burned or otherwise injured from an explosion the investigator should question the victim:

   (A) as soon as possible before he dies
   (B) wait until the victim is better so drugs and pain won't make him incoherent
   (C) don't talk to the victim; talk to other witnesses
   (D) ask the victim's doctor

85. Which of the following is incorrect:

   (A) an experienced person may be able to testify in court (concerning a gas explosion) that in his opinion, his sense of smell indicated a certain type of fuel
   (B) it is best to utilize a gas vacuum collection tube to collect air samples from where the gas odor is strongest, to be examined at the laboratory by a gas chromatograph
   (C) polyethylene bags can be used to transport porous material containing inflammables to the laboratory
   (D) a good indication of a gas explosion where gas has accumulated inside a partitioned wall is that after the explosion each side of the wall will go in different directions, similarly, collapsing of sealed metal cans equally on all sides indicates explosion of gas vapor on all sides

86. In a gas explosion the following characteristics may be found:

   (A) a ball of flame and immediate burning of tinder
   (B) no burning
   (C) victims burned
   (D) victims unburned
   (E) all of the above

87. Gasoline is easiest to ignite in explosions of what type of explosives:

   (A) black powder
   (B) dynamite
   (C) C4
   (D) nitroglycerine

88. Which statement is true:

    (A) Liquid petroleum is lighter than air
    (B) Liquid petroleum is heavier than air
    (C) Gasoline vapors are lighter than air
    (D) Gas vapors will distribute uniformly in air

89. A bomb explosion is characterized by:

    (A) pushing effects
    (B) implosion effects
    (C) a central shattering effect or pressure effects where the bomb was
    (D) fragments

90. Which of the following statements is incorrect:

    (A) craters may give a good indication of the type and quantity of explosive used
    (B) brisance refers to the shattering effect of the explosive
    (C) a high-velocity explosive has less shattering effect than a low-velocity explosive
    (D) low-velocity explosives on dirt will make craters of wide diameter and shallow depth
    (E) high-velocity explosion craters will have steep sides; low-velocity explosions will cause a crater with gradually sloping sides

91. The term for shattering effect is:

    (A) spaulding
    (B) brisance
    (C) heat pressure
    (D) breaking
    (E) pulverizing

92. Examinations of the characteristics of the metal container of an explosive will indicate the velocity of the explosive. Which of the following are the characteristics which will be examined:

    (A) number of fragments
    (B) shape of fragments
    (C) hardness of fragments
    (D) size of fragments
    (E) all the foregoing

ANSWERS

1. (A) Placing the charge on top will make it easier to find the pieces. P. 86

2. (B) Usually a testing to show that the material does explode is sufficient, however, chemical analysis is helpful. Some explosive should be retained as evidence if the court wishes to see it. P. 85

3. (D) This is the standard warning in blasting areas. P. 87

4. (A) Nitrogen will stop clocks and kill batteries temporarily. P. 88

5. (A) The X-ray produces the invisible rays which penetrate the bomb to show relative densities and are made visible by the fluoroscope viewed by the operator. P. 89

6. (C) Place bulk explosives like dynamite away from blasting caps and triggering devices since the latter two are more liable to explode accidentally. P. 90

7. (C) There have been accidents in which the fault was in the user because the blaster violated this safety rule. P. 91

8. (B) The second bomb technician, at a safe distance, should take two oblique photographs of the car, showing both sides, front, rear, license tag and location of the vehicle. P. 92

9. (D) When searching a car bombing scene this is where the center of the explosion usually is. P. 92

10. (B) The first technician should walk around the vehicle and make a general observation of the vehicle without touching it. He should examine the vehicle for possible pull wires attached from a bomb on the vehicle to a fixed object, for remote control wires, for a burning fuse, or for pressure-release devices under the wheels. P. 92

11. (B) If the victim is killed by the bomb he won't be able to pay off. P. 94

12. (A) Metal bends or breaks in the direction the force of the explosion is moving. P. 94

13. (D) Figure 84 indicates an automobile in which fragments from an explosion traveled 600 feet. Pp. 96,97

14. (E) Bombs may be initiated in one or more different methods. P. 97

15. (D) The hood of the automobile may be raised by remote control, using ropes, levers, and fulcrums. P. 97

16. (C) The right rear door is usually the least commonly used door on an automobile. Therefore, after complete observation of the right rear door area from both outside the car, and examination inside from outside the opposite side of the car, the technician should, if nothing unusual is noted, enter by this door. P. 98

17. (D) No matter how simple the bomb appears move it remotely first. P. 98

18. (E) A bomb can be found any place. P. 99

19. (E) Never tell anybody there is no bomb in a car or location after a reasonable search. Just tell them you didn't find one.   P. 100

20. (E) They may all give erroneous guesses.   P. 101

21. (B) The bomb technician should carefully examine the item before touching it, since the explosive may be a bomb, or booby trap or decoy for the real bomb, and the person at the scene may not realize it. Movement of items around it may explode the bomb accidentally.   P. 102

22. (C) If untrained police officers are handling bombs give them more training why they shouldn't.   P. 102

23. (C) Take a pea-sized sample and place it on a piece of paper. The remainder should be placed at a safe distance. The paper should be lit and the flame observed as it approaches the suspected material. The specialist stands back approximately three feet. If the material flares up, torches, or sparkles, it should be treated as an explosive. Some explosives are difficult to ignite, however, and if the sample does not burn, one cannot conclude that the specimen is not explosive. Pp. 102,103

24. (B) These two chemicals should not be mixed.   P. 103

25. (D) A hypergolic mixture is composed of two substances which may explode upon being mixed together.   P. 103

26. (A) Violent reaction is an understatement. A stronger warning is needed.   P. 104

27. (A) Sodium, upon contact with water, will explode.   P. 105

28. (C) White, yellow and red. White and yellow are found in sticks and are stored under water. Red is a dry powder.   P. 105

29. (E) The more explosives used in an area the more explosives will be recovered by the bomb squad, therefore, good control is needed. P. 106

30. (E) All these items should be included, if possible; if the material is too sensitive for much handling, items may be dispensed with. If included in the report, they may help solve a theft or apprehend bombers.   P. 106

31. (B) You need caps to set off dynamite. Search the area closely for them if a bulk explosive is found.   P. 107

32. (E) These items, plus labels, tags on the wires, etc., color of writing, colors of wires and labels, and the color of the flash powder inside the fuse will all assist in their identification. Identification may assist in clearing up cases of theft, or bombings.   Pp. 107,108

33. (A) New York City required dynamite cartridges to be numbered for identification in case of theft or recovered explosives.   P. 109

34. (D) The best determination is examination of the core at the end. If the core is black, it is safety fuse.   P. 110

35. (D) The company, located in Simsbury, Connecticut, also makes most of the detonating cord, too.   P. 110

36. (C)   Thirty three minutes is the maximum delay however in event of misfires one should wait at least one hour after the scheduled time of the explosion before approaching the charge.   P. 111

37. (D)   The explosives companies all send samples of their latest products to the FBI Laboratory's Explosive Section.   P. 113

38. (D)   The insulation varies widely in all colors.   P. 113

39. (A)   Electric caps or detonating cord would have to be used by the bomber unless there was a sympathetic explosion in which an explosion set off the other explosive.   P. 113

40. (A)   All of the other statements are true.   P. 115

41. (D)   The text gives examples of all of these.   P. 114-117

42. (D)   If a state has this law and then if all the bomb evidence is destroyed and then if you are lucky you might be able to catch your subject with this one.   P. 117

43. (B)   The word explosives is found on all dynamite boxes and cartridges.   P. 118

44. (E)   Dynamite is always packaged in fifty-pound cases or in large cylindrical cartridges. with the diameter and weight stamped upon them.   P. 118

45. (E)   In this condition the nitroglycerine floats in the water and is less likely to explode, but if the water evaporates after oozing or the nitroglycerine separates from the water, then it is more sensitive. P. 119

46. (D)   All these items are possible in improper storage of dynamite.   Pp. 119-122

47. (D)   Old dynamite is found in both conditions and sensitivity varies.   P. 120

48. (E)   Reproduction of an exploded bomb can reveal many things. P. 121

49. (D)   Nitro carbo nitrate is basically dynamite without nitroglycerine and is called a blasting agent or an oxidizer.   P. 122

50. (D)   Ammonium nitrate usually only requires a small amount of fuel.   P. 122

51. (C)   For best results with most NCN mixtures.   P. 123

52. (C)   All known boosters are cylinders and have a hole in the center for insertion of a blasting cap or detonation cord.   P. 124

53. (B)   This is used in some primers or boosters.   P. 124

54. (D)   These are all statements made on page 124.

55. (D)   The book doesn't tell how to make explosives or bombs but tells how to dispose of them and investigate them.   P. 124

56. (C)   A homemade shape used on a ship is shown in the text. P. 125

57. (C)   Nitroglycerine is very sweet to the taste, not salty.   P. 126

58. (B)   Nitroglycerine dilates the blood vessels and caffeine constricts the blood vessels.   P. 127

59. (B)   #4 and #6 are incorrect. The nitroglycerine may be poured into the desensitizer, or vice versa; washing down a safe or bank vault door which has been loaded with nitroglycerine is a very difficult job, for nitroglycerine will seep into narrow cracks and screw threads. P. 127

60. (D)   All of these are problems to be dealt with.   P. 127

61. (A)   Dynamite averages about 12,000 feet per second. The others explode about 26,000 feet per second.   P. 128

62. (C)   Safe burglaries with explosives in the United States are rare, however, in London there are about 70 a year.   Pp. 129,130

63. (C)   The name of this explosive is astrolite.   P. 128

64. (A)   Kinetic explosives are those that are shipped, similar to Astrolite, in separate containers, the contents of which, when mixed, are explosive, but which separately are safe enough for transportation by commercial transportation.   P. 129

65. (C)   Military ordnance has rendering safe procedures (RSP) for almost each item.   P. 130

66. (B)   This statement is incorrect.   Pp. 136-138

67. (A)   Blue is practice, olive drab with yellow is high explosive and gray is chemical.   P. 131

68. (D)   The explosive ordnance disposal personnel at the closest base.   P. 131

69. (B)   Make sure the safety lever can fly clear when taping the grenade and straighten the cotter pin carefully, place a piece of C4 with an electric blasting cap in it in case there is a misfire so the grenade can be exploded without having to reapproach it.   P. 133

70. (D)   A ruler is needed for reference.   P. 133

71. (A)   Package bombs are usually portable booby traps.   P. 135

72. (D)   The motive is unknown.   P. 138

73. (C)   Next to the bomber's demise this is the most reliable cure. P. 139

74. (E,D)   A bomb may be preceded by one of these but not necessarily.   P. 139

75. (A)   As in most criminal investigations, the victim is a possible suspect.   P. 139

76. (C)   Statistics disclose this.   P. 139

77. (A)   On many bombings more than one bomb may be used. P. 142

78. (A)   This is the fastest way. Otherwise, examination of any blast area for signs of a distinctive explosive. This examination can be tedious and time-consuming.   Pp. 143-146

79. (B)   The main reason for misfires with fuse caps is a faulty crimp of the cap to the fuse.   P. 147

80. (E)   The main reason for misfires with electric caps is faulty wiring connections or dead batteries.   P. 147

81. (D)   The fuse must be cut straight and be touching the flash compound.   P. 147

82. (A)   Only a small amount of gasoline is necessary.   P. 148

83. (C)   At an explosion scene, gas vapors will collect in different areas due to wind and confinement in structures. This will cause inconsistencies in effects and propagation of the explosive wave.   P. 149

84. (A)   The investigator owes it to the victim, his family and society for insurance purposes and for the prevention of future incidents.   P. 150

85. (C)   Polyethylene bags cannot be used to transport porous material containing inflammables, as they will allow the fumes to escape.   Pp. 152,153

86. (E)   Gas explosions sometimes have completely contrasting effects.   P. 153

87. (B)   Black powder will ignite gasoline easily.   P. 154

88. (B)   LP is heavier than air. All of the other statements are erroneous.   Pp. 154,155

89. (C)   A central shattering effect where the bomb was.   P. 156

90. (C)   A high-velocity explosive has a more shattering effect than a low-velocity explosion.   Pp. 156-159

91. (B)   Brisance is a shattering effect.   P. 157

92. (E) These are the four characteristics of the metal which will indicate the velocity of the explosive.   P. 162

SECTION III

Answers to the following questions may be verified in "Explosives and Bomb Disposal Guide," by Robert R. Lenz.

1. An explosion may best be defined as:
   - (A) a violent expansion or bursting resulting from a sudden production or release of pressure
   - (B) the releasing of tremendous energy engendered by internal violent heat waves
   - (C) a detonation or deflagration of energy rapidly expanded by compound gases
   - (D) extremely high temperatures, loud noise, and an external expansion of pressure

2. Most characteristic of the aftermath of an explosion is:
   - (A) detonation, extreme heat, and violent and intense shock waves
   - (B) audible sound waves, deflagration of material, and high temperatures
   - (C) a loud noise, high temperature, and usually a large volume of gas
   - (D) vapor dissemination, extreme heat, and a loud noise

3. Explosions are normally classified as being mechanical, chemical, and:
   - (A) pressure
   - (B) plastic
   - (C) nitrate
   - (D) nuclear

4. Explosives are .... compounds found in a solid, liquid, or gaseous form.
   - (A) unstable chemical
   - (B) rapid conversion
   - (C) combustible propellant
   - (D) mixed incendiary

5. A steam boiler with a defective safety device exploded, creating a rupture of the case. This type explosion would be classified as:
   - (A) mechanical
   - (B) chemical
   - (C) functional
   - (D) accidental

6. Where gases result from an extremely rapid conversion of a liquid or solid compound, we have an explosion classified as:
   - (A) cavitation
   - (B) chemical
   - (C) incendiary
   - (D) reactionary

65

7. Explosive compounds which undergo a chemical type explosion are common to:

    (A) amateur homemade
    (B) military munitions
    (C) professional
    (D) envelope bombs

8. Chemical explosions are normally accompanied by:

    (A) loud noise, radiation, and bright light
    (B) tremendous energy, extreme heat, and light
    (C) radiation, heat, and violent shock
    (D) extreme heat, loud noise, and at times, violent shock

9. Explosives, when heated, struck, or shocked by another explosive, are capable of producing an explosion by:

    (A) liberating tremendous amounts of radiation
    (B) means of ultra-high sound waves
    (C) the freeing of large amounts of heated gas
    (D) the rapid burning of combustible material

10. How quickly an explosive compound decomposes or explodes will usually determine its:

    (A) type
    (B) density
    (C) munition
    (D) function

11. Explosives are unstable substances and are always:

    (A) in an inert stage
    (B) opposed to deflagration
    (C) chemically unbalanced
    (D) attempting to stabilize

12. Normally, explosives are classified as being of three types: primary high, secondary high, and:

    (A) ignition
    (B) percussion
    (C) low
    (D) friction

13. Explosives being unstable will, therefore, when subjected to the correct initiations, become stable either by:

    (A) exploding or violent concussions
    (B) rapid burning or detonation
    (C) instant combustion or slow burning
    (D) deflagration or changing compounds

14. Low explosives are often referred to as the "burning explosives" and an example would be:

   (A) blasting caps
   (B) TNT
   (C) dynamite
   (D) black powder

15. The most accurate statement that can be said about the low explosives is they are usually:

   (A) not designed for violent explosion
   (B) designed to detonate by shock
   (C) extremely sensitive to heat waves
   (D) ignited by means of an electric charge

16. Bombs and explosives of the low explosive type are often used by psychotics and saboteurs because of their:

   (A) low cost
   (B) destructive power
   (C) availability
   (D) compact size

17. The initiation of low explosives is:

   (A) relatively simple
   (B) moderately difficult
   (C) extremely complex
   (D) usually by friction

18. In most cases the initiation of low explosives is achieved by:

   (A) inflammation or fire
   (B) a spark or flame
   (C) electrical charge
   (D) a simple detonation

19. The type explosives classified as primary high are extremely sensitive to:

   (A) rough handling
   (B) changing temperatures
   (C) exposure to water
   (D) heat, shock, or friction

20. Primary high explosives under normal conditions will:

   (A) burn rapidly
   (B) detonate rapidly
   (C) create little shock
   (D) be soundless

21. Primary high explosives are often referred to as primers or detonators and in most cases provide the main ingredient in:
    (A) TNT
    (B) dynamite
    (C) blasting caps
    (D) gun powder

22. Experience indicates that primary high explosives are:
    (A) almost impossible to improvise outside of laboratory conditions
    (B) used to a great extent by psychotics and saboteurs
    (C) relatively easy to manufacture in small quantities
    (D) procured mostly by means of truck hijacking

23. The usual purpose of primary high explosives is to:
    (A) act as a primary for percussion caps
    (B) detonate secondary high explosives
    (C) ignite an explosive electrically
    (D) provide the abrasive for friction primers

24. The vast number of high explosives are classified as:
    (A) primary high explosives
    (B) inflammation explosives
    (C) percussion explosives
    (D) secondary high explosives

25. Secondary high explosives are relatively:
    (A) unstable, and will easily detonate or burn
    (B) sensitive to heat and chemicals
    (C) insensitive to heat, shock, or friction
    (D) stable, and will seldom burn

26. An example of a secondary high explosive is:
    (A) blasting caps
    (B) rifle powder
    (C) black powder
    (D) dynamite

27. Secondary high explosives will usually burn rather than detonate if ignited in limited quantities in the open air. For this reason, they are used primarily as:
    (A) booster and main bursting charges
    (B) detonating and priming devices
    (C) electrically timed ignition charges
    (D) percussion and detonating devices

28. When manufacturing secondary high explosives, the average individual will find them:

(A) impossible to manufacture
(B) easy to improvise
(C) difficult to manufacture
(D) easy to manufacture

29. Explosions do not just happen, they require:

(A) oxygen, heat, and controlled conditions
(B) an initiating procedure to induce the result
(C) a rapid burning of relevant materials
(D) conditions allowing for gases to escape

30. Where the explosive is fired by an electrically heated wire, we have a method of initiating an explosive known as:

(A) ignition
(B) inflammation
(C) percussion
(D) friction

31. When an explosive is fired by a flame produced from a fuse, we have a method of initiating an explosive known as:

(A) ignition
(B) friction
(C) percussion
(D) inflammation

32. When a main charge is detonated or ignited by the striking of percussion caps and primers, we have a method of initiating an explosive known as:

(A) friction
(B) percussion
(C) detonation
(D) ignition

33. A good example of percussion is:

(A) a spark inside an automobile engine which explodes the gas vapors
(B) the igniting of a fuse similar to that used in common firecrackers
(C) a rifle's firing pin striking a percussion cap and igniting the propellant
(D) a strong shock wave initiated by the excessive force of gases

34. The method of initiating an explosive by means of a type of abrasion is known as:

(A) percussion
(B) friction
(C) ignition
(D) inflammation

35. The method of initiating an explosive where a strong shock wave set up by primary and secondary high explosives causes the explosive to detonate at its maximum force is known as:

(A) percussion
(B) ignition
(C) detonation
(D) inflammation

36. An excellent example of material needed for detonating initiation is:

(A) dynamite primed with a blasting cap
(B) gas vapors ignited by a hot wire
(C) when a firecracker fuse is lighted
(D) friction resulting from abrasion

37. The process of building up extremely high voltages and suddenly releasing it into certain types of thin wire, causing the wire to explode and thereby detonate a high explosive, is known as:

(A) ignition detonation
(B) exploding wire detonation
(C) inflammation detonation
(D) percussion detonation

38. The terms "high order" and "low order" when used by bomb disposal technicians during disposal operations, refers to the manner in which the explosives they are dealing with:

(A) burn
(B) ignite
(C) detonate
(D) propel

39. The term "high order detonation" indicates an explosive:

(A) device detonated at a lower than maximum output
(B) device, from malfunction, was incomplete
(C) detonated at a rate higher than was anticipated
(D) completely detonated at its maximum velocity

40. The term "low order detonation" indicates incomplete or detonation at a less than maximum expected rate. This condition would least likely be caused by:

    (A) deterioration
    (B) a separation of components
    (C) improper initiator
    (D) faulty friction

41. It is common to find when low order detonation takes place the:

    (A) area around the site of detonation will have chunks or powdered explosive
    (B) fault can be traced to a powder delay in the action train
    (C) entire mass of explosives was consumed at an uneven rate of speed
    (D) basic propellant resulted from a delay in the powder or primer

42. Most explosives and explosions require a firing train to achieve initiation. Explosion is achieved by small amounts of energy increasing in size and force. In the basic propellant train, the initial force originates from the:

    (A) detonator
    (B) primer
    (C) propelling charge
    (D) igniter charge

43. The sensitivity of an explosive is normally determined by:

    (A) chemical reaction
    (B) temperature change
    (C) ease of initiation
    (D) reaction time

44. Most explosives are:

    (A) not subject to desensitizing
    (B) subject to one level of desensitizing
    (C) sensitive only to exposure to oxygen
    (D) desensitized to a certain degree

45. Desensitizing of explosives, when it takes place, usually occurs:

    (A) in the manufacturing process
    (B) when left alone for long periods of time
    (C) when exposed to low temperatures
    (D) when exposed to moisture

71

46. A good example of an explosive compound that can change chemically to render it so sensitive that human body heat could detonate it is:

   (A)   packaged ammonium nitrate exposed to moisture
   (B)   dynamite when the blasting caps are removed
   (C)   a metallic container of badly decomposed nitroglycerine
   (D)   smokeless black powder when introduced to potassium

47. When explosives are melted, poured, and cooled in a container, they form a solid and provide what is known as a:

   (A)   low oxidizing explosive
   (B)   high density explosive
   (C)   double based propellant
   (D)   single purpose lacrymate

48. The degree of explosive sensitivity is usually controlled prior to shipping by the manufacturer. A factor that would least affect the sensitivity of an explosive is:

   (A)   density
   (B)   temperature
   (C)   moisture
   (D)   the detonator

49. Specifications on or with explosives are used:

   (A)   to identify the manufacturer
   (B)   for purposes of disarming
   (C)   for bombs containing dynamite
   (D)   as a guide for the users

50. Explosives dangerous for handling may result from certain chemical changes, least of which is:

   (A)   reaction with certain metals
   (B)   density of material
   (C)   temperature changes
   (D)   chemical reactions

51. Powdering of high explosives in containers can be extremely dangerous when caused by:

   (A)   rough handling
   (B)   inactivity
   (C)   container oxidation
   (D)   decomposition

52. Most military secondary high explosives are required by specifications to be:

   (A) sensitive to temperature changes and moisture
   (B) relatively insensitive to friction or heat shock
   (C) interchangeable with many other type explosives
   (D) insensitive to fuse and charge displacement

53. When an explosive compound is kept for a long period of time in unstable storage, it can form explosive gases and salts, which now, because of its erratic nature, could cause it to spontaneously ignite or detonate when handled. This action most accurately describes:

   (A) a chemical reaction
   (B) a time detonation
   (C) induced inflammation
   (D) propellant ignition

54. When an explosive is melted, poured, and cooled into the actual container, it is said to have been:

   (A) press loaded
   (B) block fitted
   (C) cast loaded
   (D) extrusion loaded

55. Most military high explosives are:

   (A) block fitted
   (B) cast loaded
   (C) extrusion loaded
   (D) press loaded

56. Which of the below is not a method for loading explosives into ammunition or packing it into containers:

   (A) cast loaded
   (B) press loaded
   (C) block fitted
   (D) insert knolling

57. Most explosives and devices must be destroyed by:

   (A) the application of an explosive against an explosive
   (B) prolonged exposure to extremely low temperatures
   (C) immersion in low viscosity lubricating oil
   (D) the utilization of underground testing areas

73

58. The best way to train personnel in bomb disposal techniques is:
    (A) to observe experts in the field actually disarming a bomb
    (B) the study of books and manuals on demolition
    (C) actual field training using demolition materials
    (D) to send them to the factories where the bombs are produced

59. The fear of handling demolition materials can only be overcome by:
    (A) familiarization and close contact
    (B) observing successful deactivations
    (C) the knowledge of how a bomb is made
    (D) knowing the exact procedure for deactivation

60. Blasting caps are grouped into two main categories, electric and:
    (A) mechanical
    (B) non-electric
    (C) extrusion
    (D) chemical

61. Blasting caps, regardless of their size, are very dangerous and are sensitive to shock, friction, and:
    (A) water
    (B) heat
    (C) solvents
    (D) light

62. Blasting caps are normally initiated by means of electrical wires with battery power or:
    (A) a single charge primer
    (B) acid fulminate
    (C) a burning time fuse
    (D) controlled shock waves

63. Most blasting caps can be described as being the diameter of:
    (A) ¼ inch and range in length from one to six inches
    (B) one inch and having a length of one to two inches
    (C) two inches and shaped like a ball
    (D) two inches and rarely more than one inch in length

64. Detonating cord (primacord) actually initiates an explosive by:
    (A) the extraneous use of electricity
    (B) using infra-red heat waves
    (C) distorting the chemical crystals
    (D) transmission of a detonating wave

65. Blasting caps can at times be dangerous; a safer substitute is:

(A) shaped cord
(B) detonating cord
(C) photoflash powder
(D) a timing switch

66. The core of a length of detonating cord (primacord) contains:

(A) a powerful explosive
(B) electrical wires
(C) inert material
(D) a liquid propellant

67. A quality not usually found in detonating cord is:

(A) resistance to extraneous electricity
(B) insensitivity to heat
(C) safety during blasting operations
(D) relative susceptibility to shock

68. Igniters are used mostly to ignite rocket motors, simulators, noise makers, and:

(A) blasting caps
(B) nitroglycerine
(C) black powder devices
(D) gelatin dynamite

69. Igniters are usually manufactured in a:

(A) glass pressure device
(B) plastic or metallic container
(C) compressed paper tube
(D) baked porcelain container

70. The majority of igniters are of the:

(A) electrical variety
(B) mechanical type
(C) photoflash variety
(D) chemical type

71. A medium through which fire is transported at a continuous and uniform rate to a non-electric blasting cap or explosive charge is known as a/an:

(A) igniter
(B) pressure plug
(C) main charge
(D) safety fuse

72. Least characteristic of a safety fuse is:
   (A) it is slightly smaller in diameter than a blasting cap
   (B) it is usually sold or issued in 50 foot coiled lengths
   (C) the fuse has a waxy appearance and varies in color
   (D) burning time averages over one minute per foot

73. A tool known as a cap crimper would be most useful:
   (A) disarming a faulty cap from the main explosive
   (B) securely fastening a blasting cap to a safety fuse
   (C) cutting the electrical wires leading from the blasting cap
   (D) splitting the positive and negative charge wires

74. Cap crimpers are most essential for safety and efficiency in all blasting operations except:
   (A) non-electric
   (B) electric
   (C) mechanical
   (D) safety fuse

75. Cap crimpers are normally constructed of a:
   (A) hard carbon steel
   (B) chrome plated metal
   (C) non-sparking type metal
   (D) low gloss brushed steel

76. Blasting machines are used to generate current for:
   (A) firing electric blasting caps
   (B) firing a charge through a safety fuse
   (C) setting off nitroglycerine
   (D) igniting double based propellants

77. The greater majority of blasting machines are:
   (A) functional magnetos
   (B) reconditioned batteries
   (C) modified generators
   (D) compact alternators

78. Blasting machines are usually rated by:
   (A) the number of copper wire electric caps that they will fire in a straight series circuit
   (B) their capacity to store and discharge electric current upon demand
   (C) their detonating capability from point of charge to machine
   (D) the number of circuit blasters capable of receiving generated current

79. A blasting machine will range in its capacity of initiation from:
   (A) one blasting cap to ten
   (B) one blasting cap to one hundred
   (C) five blasting caps to fifty
   (D) five blasting caps to ten

80. The slang term used by many disposal workers for the blasting machine is the:
   (A) pop cover
   (B) Dante's Inferno
   (C) plumber's friend
   (D) hell box

81. A fuse lighter is designed to provide:
   (A) a method of checking fuses for circuit damage
   (B) a small current generated by a chloride battery
   (C) a quick, sure method of igniting safety fuse
   (D) ignition by means of a flame or sulphuric acid

82. The two most common types of fuse lighters are the:
   (A) ram projectile and the hand percussion
   (B) automatic cocked pin and the pull wire type
   (C) single and double based propellants
   (D) galvanometer and collapsing circuit

83. Another name for a circuit tester is a:
   (A) photoelectric device
   (B) fluoroscope
   (C) altimeter
   (D) galvanometer

84. A circuit tester is used by blasters to test a circuit:
   (A) prior and after initiation to determine the amount of current generated
   (B) after initiation to determine if all circuits fired on schedule
   (C) during initiation to determine the galvanic response to the electric current
   (D) prior to initiation to determine if the circuit is complete for firing

85. A circuit tester will indicate the existence of short circuits or leaks and the:
   (A) approximate resistance of a circuit
   (B) approximate resistance to percussion
   (C) igniting mixture used in the explosive filler
   (D) sensitivity to internal and external forces

86. Usually current is generated in a circuit tester by a:

   (A) permanent galvanometer
   (B) crystal magneto
   (C) silver chloride battery
   (D) reverse type generator

87. When designated igniters, detonators, and burning fuses are not available, improvised substitutes are often used. Not an example of an improvised device or substance issued as an igniter is:

   (A) light bulbs
   (B) potassium chlorate
   (C) glo-plugs
   (D) firework fuses

88. A light bulb is discovered partially filled with black powder and wires soldered to its base extending outward. From experience they would know this device is probably an improvised:

   (A) detonator
   (B) igniter
   (C) fuse
   (D) circuit

89. Potassium chlorate and sugar are used widely as an improvised igniter mixture or at times explosive fillers. These can be easily ignited by:

   (A) sulphuric acid delay mechanisms or flame
   (B) electrical current or natural oxidation
   (C) exposure to nitrates and radio waves
   (D) frictional guncotton and trinitolonene

90. A small spark plug called a glo-plug is sometimes used as an improvised igniter and is most readily found in a/an:

   (A) automobile parts department
   (B) lawnmower repair shop
   (C) model aircraft hobby shop
   (D) farm implement repair shop

91. An improvised electrical or mechanical device designed to initiate an incendiary explosive by means of a brisk flame is a type of:

   (A) fuse
   (B) igniter
   (C) detonator
   (D) primer

92. We find a shotgun shell with a slug removed and the open end closed with wadding and an improvised firing pin mechanism set up. This improvised percussion type igniter is often used by:

    (A) mine demolition experts working several hundred feet below sea level
    (B) professional terrorists and saboteurs to ignite black powder bombs and incendiary devices
    (C) engineers clearing roadways through dense jungle terrain or swampy areas
    (D) criminals when attempting to eliminate clandestine alarm systems

93. One of the more common improvised time fuses is:

    (A) nylon finger dipped in a solution of nitroglycerine
    (B) model airplane glue combined with heads of matches
    (C) a mixture of airplane glue and sulphur inserted in a drinking straw
    (D) cotton string impregnated with solutions of potassium chlorate and sugar

94. Which of the below is not a commonly improvised time fuse:

    (A) assorted commercial firework fuses
    (B) a mixture of household glue and black powder impregnated on cotton string
    (C) a mixture of potassium permanganate, flour, and sulfur inserted into a common drinking straw
    (D) a mixture of sulfur, mineral oil, and ammonium nitrate impregnated on nylon string

95. It is most difficult to improvise a/an:

    (A) time fuse
    (B) igniter
    (C) detonator
    (D) black powder bomb

96. Primers are usually small devices containing a priming mixture which are used to:

    (A) produce fire or a small explosion
    (B) provide bulk quantity of inert material
    (C) trigger electric and mechanical blasting caps
    (D) measure the sensitivity of the blasting charge

97. Generally, igniters that cause initiation are grouped into two types, namely:

    (A) fuse and detonator
    (B) detonator and primer
    (C) friction and flame
    (D) percussion or friction

98. The best example of a primer device is:

    (A) the small string-like fuse leading from commercial fireworks
    (B) a blasting cap used to detonate larger explosives
    (C) the small round primer at the center base of a shotgun shell
    (D) ammunition used in standard small arm weapons

99. Police officers generally encounter:

    (A) Navy explosives
    (B) Army explosives
    (C) commercial explosives
    (D) homemade explosives

100. Saboteurs and psychotics usually resort to stealing explosives from:

    (A) civilian construction sites
    (B) military bases
    (C) explosive factories
    (D) wholesale explosive centers

QUES.	ANS.	PAGE	QUES.	ANS.	PAGE
1.	A	14	23.	B	16
2.	C	14	24.	D	16
3.	D	14,15	25.	C	16
4.	A	15	26.	D	16
5.	A	15	27.	A	16
6.	B	15	28.	C	16
7.	B	15	29.	B	17
8.	D	15	30.	A	17
9.	C	15	31.	D	17
10.	A	15	32.	B	17
11.	D	15	33.	C	17
12.	C	15	34.	B	17
13.	B	15	35.	C	17
14.	D	15	36.	A	17
15.	A	15	37.	B	17
16.	C	15,16	38.	C	17
17.	A	16	39.	D	18
18.	B	16	40.	D	18
19.	D	16	41.	A	18
20.	B	16	42.	B	18,19
21.	C	16	43.	C	20
22.	A	16	44.	C	20

QUES.	ANS.	PAGE	QUES.	ANS.	PAGE
45.	A	20	68.	C	28
46.	C	20	69.	B	28
47.	B	21	70.	A	28
48.	D	21	71.	D	28
49.	D	21	72.	D	28
50.	B	21	73.	B	30
51.	A	21	74.	B	30
52.	B	21	75.	C	30
53.	A	21	76.	A	30
54.	C	21	77.	C	30
55.	B	21	78.	A	30,31
56.	D	21,22	79.	B	31
57.	A	23	80.	D	31
58.	C	23	81.	C	32
59.	A	23	82.	B	32
60.	B	24	83.	D	32
61.	B	24	84.	D	32
62.	C	24	85.	A	32
63.	A	24	86.	C	32
64.	D	26	87.	D	33
65.	B	26	88.	B	33
66.	A	26	89.	A	33
67.	C	27	90.	C	33

QUES.	ANS.	PAGE	QUES.	ANS.	PAGE
91.	B	33			
92.	B	33,34			
93.	D	34			
94.	D	34			
95.	C	34			
96.	A	34			
97.	D	34			
98.	C	34			
99.	C	35			
100.	A	35			

SECTION IV

1. The color of black powder is usually:

    (A) very dull black
    (B) shiny black, or brown
    (C) very dull gray
    (D) dull gray or black

2. Disposal of the commercial explosive (low) black powder is usually accomplished by:

    (A) detonating underground or disposal in abandoned mines
    (B) burning or dumping into a fast moving stream of water
    (C) sealing in containers and storing in unusable salt mines
    (D) sealing in large aluminum containers and dropping them at sea

3. Generally considered the most dangerous explosive known is:

    (A) ammonium nitrate
    (B) picric acid
    (C) mercury fulminate
    (D) black powder

4. Black powder is generally considered to be the most dangeroue explosive known because of its:

    (A) sensitivity
    (B) explosive power
    (C) manifold uses
    (D) accessibility

5. Single base commercial smokeless powder is usually disposed of by:

    (A) immersion in oil
    (B) detonation
    (C) burning
    (D) oxidation

6. Saboteurs, psychotics, and safecrackers make extensive use of dynamite primarily because:

    (A) of its insensitive reaction to heat
    (B) of its availability and shocking power
    (C) there is no initiation required for explosion
    (D) nitroglycerine is too unstable for use

7. Dynamites are most often used commercially as a blasting agent and can be grouped into certain basic types, one of which is not:

   (A) straight dynamite
   (B) blasting gelatin
   (C) military dynamite
   (D) nitrate dynamite

8. All dynamites contain nitroglycerine except:

   (A) gelatin dynamite
   (B) ammonia dynamite
   (C) military dynamite
   (D) low freezing dynamite

9. A label on a stick of dynamite that indicated 40% would mean:

   (A) that stick contains 40% of nitroglycerine by weight
   (B) the dynamite contains 40% inert and non-explosive material
   (C) the detonating velocity of the dynamite is 40% capacity
   (D) it contains 40% black or smokeless powder

10. Dynamite requires:

    (A) non-electric detonator initiation
    (B) a desensitized method of initiation
    (C) the detonating velocity be less than 4,000 feet per second
    (D) initiation by a detonator

11. Most dynamite is:

    (A) sensitive only to heat
    (B) sensitive to bullet impact, friction, and heat
    (C) insensitive, and detonation is possible only with a cap
    (D) sensitive only to impact and heat

12. Color varies in dynamite; however, most will be a:

    (A) reddish pink or dark red
    (B) black or dark gray
    (C) dull gray or charcoal black
    (D) reddish yellow to brownish yellow

13. Dynamite comes in many diameters and comes in lengths as long as:

    (A) 35 inches
    (B) 30 inches
    (C) 40 inches
    (D) 50 inches

14. Most cases of dynamite are constructed of wood or fiberboard and shipped:

    (A) in 5 pound packages
    (B) 24 pounds to the case
    (C) 50 pounds to the case
    (D) 100 pounds to the case

15. Recently a substitute used in place of nitroglycerine is:

    (A) ammonium nitrate
    (B) chemical fougasse
    (C) trinitrotoluene
    (D) picric acid

16. When ammonium nitrate is confined, moisture and excessively high temperatures will form dangerous:

    (A) ammonia crystals
    (B) ammonia fumes
    (C) ammonium trinitrotoluene
    (D) ammonium phosphate

17. Ammonium nitrate is commonly used as:

    (A) cough medicine
    (B) rifle powder
    (C) a paint additive
    (D) fertilizer

18. If properly mixed, ammonium nitrate explosives can be compared in strength to a:

    (A) 20% nitroglycerine bomb
    (B) 75% black powder explosive
    (C) 10% military grade of TNT
    (D) 60% straight dynamite mixture

19. What makes ammonium nitrate of concern to police is its:

    (A) detonating force
    (B) ease of initiation
    (C) availability
    (D) compact size

20. Glyceryl trinitrate is the chemical name for:

    (A) nitroglycerine
    (B) TNT
    (C) dynamite
    (D) tear gas

21. Glycerin is a by-product of:

    (A) perfume
    (B) soap manufacture
    (C) coal-tar elements
    (D) graphite

22. Glycerin when treated with certain substances becomes nitro-glycerin. These substances are:

    (A) amatol and ammonia
    (B) misnay and mustard nitrate
    (C) trinitrotoluene and liquid oxygen
    (D) sulphuric and nitric acid

23. In its pure form, nitroglycerin is a:

    (A) thick black paste
    (B) brownish-black powder
    (C) colorless, oily liquid
    (D) dark brown liquid

24. When mixed with impurities, nitroglycerin changes and becomes a:

    (A) milky to yellow oily liquid
    (B) thick, black lumpy paste
    (C) black powder
    (D) brownish-black liquid

25. The most common use of nitroglycerin is:

    (A) coal mining
    (B) strip mining
    (C) safe blowing
    (D) tunnel building

26. Nitroglycerin is usually found in dynamite in the per cent range of:

    (A) 40-60
    (B) 10-60
    (C) 50-80
    (D) 60-80

27. Listed are several methods criminals use to extract nitroglycerin from dynamite; the most dangerous is by:

    (A) utilizing heated salt solutions
    (B) milking the nitro using a silk stocking under hot water
    (C) boiling dynamite in water
    (D) heating dynamite on a steel plate over an open fire

28. Nitroglycerin is used as a heat stimulant and has a:
    (A) bitter taste
    (B) sweet taste
    (C) sour taste
    (D) salty taste

29. A small taste of nitroglycerin will cause:
    (A) a severe headache
    (B) temporary blindness
    (C) stomach cramps
    (D) diarrhea

30. One safe method of testing a substance to determine if it is nitroglycerin is:
    (A) pour a small quantity of the suspected substance into cool water and allow 2-5 minutes for a reaction (small beads should form on the sides of the container)
    (B) pour 5-10 drops of the suspected liquid on a metal plate and place the plate over an open fire (the drops should turn bright red and solidify)
    (C) dip one end of a ½" x 4" strip of newspaper into the substance and put on a steel object and strike with a hammer (it should sound like a firecracker explosion)
    (D) pour several drops of the suspected substance on a nylon stocking (it should immediately begin to burn away the nylon, similar to an acid reaction)

31. There are several solutions used for desensitizing or neutralizing nitroglycerin; one is:
    (A) acetone sulphide
    (B) denatured sodium
    (C) alcoholic potash
    (D) fougasse gelatin

32. Which of the below combinations, mixed effectively would neutralize nitroglycerin:
    (A) sodium sulphide, denatured alcohol, acetone, and water
    (B) sodium chloride, dextrose, and ethyl alcohol
    (C) sulfuric acid, acetone, ammonium nitrate, and alcohol
    (D) graphite, linseed oil, alcohol, and ice water

33. Experts feel that dropping or throwing nitroglycerin against something will result in a detonation about:
    (A) 5% of the time
    (B) 75% of the time
    (C) 50% of the time
    (D) 99% of the time

34. A good practice for handling nitroglycerin prior to transporting is:

    (A)   carefully pour the nitro in a plastic or rubber bottle
    (B)   to pour the nitro into a sawdust filled container
    (C)   to mix the nitro with an equal amount of black gun powder
    (D)   carefully pour the nitro into an aluminum or stainless steel container

35. If a small quantity of nitroglycerin is spilled on the floor, the wisest procedure is to:

    (A)   wash with soap and water
    (B)   not to touch it, allow it to dry on its own
    (C)   use a neutralizer or absorb with sawdust
    (D)   cover with a light coat of heavy cream

36. Pure nitroglycerin is best disposed of by:

    (A)   detonation only
    (B)   burning only
    (C)   pouring in the ocean
    (D)   detonation or burning

37. The better method of destroying desensitized nitroglycerin waste is:

    (A)   burning on a bed of sawdust
    (B)   pouring in a fast-moving stream
    (C)   burying in the ground
    (D)   put in a container and dropped in the ocean

38. The most accurate statement concerning badly decomposed nitroglycerin is:

    (A)   most of its explosive power is gone
    (B)   it will appear a deep red in color
    (C)   it may be extremely hazardous to transport
    (D)   it may emit whitish yellow fumes

39. When it occurs, perhaps the better way to know an explosion is caused by a military type explosive is by:

    (A)   its white mushroom cloud
    (B)   the type noise it makes
    (C)   a shrill whistle prior to detonation
    (D)   its shattering effect

40. Military type explosives require a special type blasting cap for detonation called:
    (A) "the McGowan Jack cap"
    (B) "a mercury fulminate cap"
    (C) "a percussion booster cap"
    (D) "the engineer special cap"

41. The double base propellants found in military type explosives are normally used as:
    (A) ignition for detonator or booster initiation
    (B) solid fuel for large rocket motors or boosters
    (C) the precipitation of excessive fulminate residue
    (D) a booster for armor piercing and high explosives

42. The reason double base propellants are more sensitive and dangerous than a single base is:
    (A) nitroglycerine is used as a solvent in their manufacture
    (B) double base propellants have over twice the amount of dynamite
    (C) nitrates and oxidizers are used in single base propellants
    (D) the addition of fougasse and ammonium in double base propellants

43. Primary high explosives are:
    (A) one of the few types of stable explosives
    (B) most often used as the main charge of an explosive
    (C) extremely sensitive to heat, shock, and friction
    (D) seldom, if ever, used in primers or for ignition purposes

44. Primary high explosives are not used:
    (A) as the main charge in military type explosives
    (B) in primers that produce ignition
    (C) in the manufacture of toy caps
    (D) in the manufacture of blasting caps

45. High explosives are extremely sensitive and the most sensitive type is called:
    (A) mercury oxide
    (B) ammonium picturn
    (C) pyrothicnic lacrymate
    (D) fulminate of silver

46. The most powerful explosive known is:
    (A) lead styphnate
    (B) P.E.T.N.
    (C) R.D.X.
    (D) lead azide

47. The primary reason most civilian concerns do not use military high explosives in bulk form is the:

   (A) high cost
   (B) high detonation required
   (C) auxiliary equipment required
   (D) per unit weight

48. The initials T.N.T. are common to most people; they are the abbreviation for:

   (A) timed-nitro-train
   (B) tri-nitro-toluene
   (C) tetryl-nitrate-toluene
   (D) tri-nitro-tetryl

49. T.N.T. is usually used as a/an:

   (A) auxiliary charge
   (B) primer charge
   (C) main charge
   (D) secondary charge

50. T.N.T. is generally considered a/an:

   (A) medium explosive
   (B) low explosive
   (C) extremely sensitive explosive
   (D) high explosive

51. T.N.T. is usually disposed of by:

   (A) detonation only
   (B) burning only
   (C) mixing with water
   (D) detonation or burning

52. Generally considered the most widely used military explosive in the United States is:

   (A) amatol
   (B) TNT
   (C) ammonium nitrate
   (D) composition "B"

53. Presently considered to be one of the most versatile type explosives is:

   (A) trinitrotoluene
   (B) liquid dynamite
   (C) sheet explosives
   (D) guncotton

54. The ingredients for making a homemade bomb are:
   (A) a fuel, a good oxidizer, and binder
   (B) a blasting cap, a composition, and pressure release
   (C) an initiating device, lacrymates, and release delay
   (D) a charge, time action, and fougasse

55. Chlorates, perchlorates, and nitrates are known as:
   (A) binders
   (B) fuels
   (C) oxidizers
   (D) igniters

56. The most widely used explosives in homemade bombs and devices are:
   (A) nitroglycerine and smokeless powder
   (B) TNT and nitroglycerin
   (C) ammonium nitrate and nitroglycerine
   (D) black and smokeless powder

57. *Black powder usually contains the following rate of ingredients:
   (A) powdered charcoal 74%, potassium nitrate 16%, sulphur 10%
   (B) sulphur 74%, potassium nitrate 10%, powdered charcoal 16%
   (C) potassium nitrate 74%, powdered charcoal 16%, sulphur 10%
   (D) potassium nitrate 10%, sulphur 74%, powdered charcoal 16%

*Note: The student interested in homemade bombs, explosives, and devices, should be aware the mixtures possible are quite large and still growing.   (See pages 61 and 62)

58. Trepanning, thermal (steaming), and chemical (solvent means) are methods used to:
   (A) remove explosives from their containers
   (B) destroy explosives and detonators
   (C) improvise homemade explosives
   (D) detonate high and low grade dynamite

59. The most important factor to know prior to steaming an explosive from its container is the:
   (A) container material
   (B) initiation sequence
   (C) type explosive
   (D) detonation rate

93

60. Which of the below explosives will detonate if the steaming method is used to separate it from its container:

    (A)   a mixture of dynamite, phosphorus, and picric acid
    (B)   a mixture of nitrate, patate, and lacrymate
    (C)   a mixture of lacrymate, fougasse, and trinitrotoluene
    (D)   a mixture of ammonium nitrate, TNT, and aluminum powder

61. Which of the below is not a solvent used to dissolve certain explosives from their containers:

    (A)   water
    (B)   fougasse
    (C)   acetone
    (D)   pyridine

62. The most accurate statement involving dumping explosives at sea is:

    (A)   many explosives are excluded from disposal at sea
    (B)   explosives are not permitted to be dumped less than 100 miles from shore
    (C)   explosives are not permitted to be dumped in less than 1000 fathoms
    (D)   all explosives may be disposed of that way

63. The preferred method of destroying high explosives is:

    (A)   detonation
    (B)   burning
    (C)   dumping at sea
    (D)   burying

64. When destroying smokeless powder by burning, do not burn more than:

    (A)   100 pounds at one time
    (B)   500 pounds at one time
    (C)   1000 pounds at one time
    (D)   2000 pounds at one time

65. When destroying dynamite by burning, the cartridges should:

    (A)   be immersed in oil
    (B)   have the caps removed
    (C)   be set in triple layers
    (D)   be slit lengthwise

66. When destroying black powder by burning, do not burn at one time more than:

    (A)   50 pounds
    (B)   100 pounds
    (C)   200 pounds
    (D)   500 pounds

67. Nitroglycerine, raw or liquid, may best be destroyed by burning if:

    (A)   in a metal container
    (B)   put in a rubber tire
    (C)   soaked in sawdust
    (D)   placed in a metal plate

68. The amount of nitroglycerine (raw or liquid) that should be destroyed by burning at one time should not exceed:

    (A)   one pint
    (B)   one quart
    (C)   one gallon
    (D)   five gallons

69. The most versatile solvent used to soften and facilitate the removal of explosives from their various containers is:

    (A)   water
    (B)   benzine
    (C)   acetone
    (D)   alcohol

70. The blast from an explosive may best be described as:

    (A)   material and debris moving outward
    (B)   a pressure wave of compressed air
    (C)   negative pressure created by a vacuum
    (D)   the outward movement of heat and shock waves

71. A fragmentation explosion will cause debris and container material to move outward:

    (A)   only in a downward direction
    (B)   only in an outward direction
    (C)   in every direction
    (D)   only in an upward direction

72. When detonated, solid blocks of explosives will:

    (A)   take the path of least resistance
    (B)   create temperatures in excess of 7000° C.
    (C)   cause a negative pressure vacuum
    (D)   always cause severe earth shock

73. Another name for a piece of pipe or tubing sealed at one end with wadding and a pipe cap on the other containing: black powder, wadding, scrap metal, and an improvised igniter, is a:

 (A) squib
 (B) fougasse
 (C) vesicant
 (D) lacrymate

74. The effect of an explosion where a large mass of explosive is placed on one side of brittle steel and its detonation causes metal from the opposite side to flake or scab off is known as the:

 (A) shrapnel effect
 (B) whistle effect
 (C) vibratory effect
 (D) scabbing effect

75. Shrapnel is often used in explosive charges and is packed in or around the charge. In military munitions, we would least likely find shrapnel take the form of:

 (A) ball bearings
 (B) cube-like devices
 (C) the letter "P"
 (D) arrow-like objects

76. When properly employed incendiary materials can be more effective than explosives because:

 (A) inflammable material has a higher incendiary effect
 (B) the target is completely consumed by fire if not controlled in time
 (C) thermite mixtures combine with iron more readily
 (D) techniques are geared towards neutralizing explosive devices

77. Incendiary devices require three essential ingredients, none of which is:

 (A) a base
 (B) fuel
 (C) kindling
 (D) an initiator (match)

78. Almost any combustible material can be used as a fuel; however, experience indicates that most professional fire-bugs and saboteurs will use:

 (A) dynamite or nitroglycerin
 (B) low grade easily obtained tissue paper
 (C) a highly inflammable material
 (D) sodium chloride or vesicant of nitrate

79. Water used to extinguish certain incendiaries may cause:
    (A) lethal gas
    (B) an explosion
    (C) a low metallic reaction
    (D) iron oxide

80. Military incendiaries are used primarily to:
    (A) set fire to buildings, industrial installations, ammunition, etc.
    (B) clear large areas of vegetation for offensive and defensive purposes
    (C) test metal for oxidation, fusing, and heat resistance
    (D) stop oil well and gas well fires

81. Military incendiaries are divided into three main groups; not included is:
    (A) oil
    (B) metal
    (C) oil and metal
    (D) picric acid

82. Natural rubber is often used as a thickening material for what type incendiary:
    (A) metal
    (B) picric acid
    (C) oil
    (D) oil and metal

83. Metal incendiaries are made from:
    (A) copper oxide, flaked aluminum, and ferrous sulfate
    (B) iron oxide, powdered aluminum, and magnesium
    (C) metallic sodium and iron phosphorus
    (D) bronze oxide and aluminum oxide

84. Two materials often used as an ignition source for oil incendiaries are:
    (A) magnesium and iron oxide
    (B) aluminum oxide and iron phosphorus
    (C) metallic sodium and white phosphorus
    (D) ferrous sulfate and aluminum oxide

85. Metal incendiaries:
    (A) ignite at low temperatures
    (B) have low melting qualities
    (C) have no ferrous material
    (D) are difficult to extinguish

97

86. Oil and metal incendiaries are often nicknamed:
 (A) "PT" mixtures
 (B) "DO" mixtures
 (C) "BL" mixtures
 (D) "TL" mixtures

87. A modern Molotov Cocktail consists of a bottle filled with:
 (A) 2/3 sulphuric acid and 1/3 gas
 (B) 1/2 gas and 1/2 kerosene
 (C) 2/3 gas and 1/3 sulphuric acid
 (D) 1/2 gas and 1/4 lamp oil

88. The fire bomb called a "snow ball" consists of:
 (A) a wax mold with sodium chloride and glycerin, with a length of safety fuse as an igniter
 (B) cellophane rolled into a tight ball dipped into carbon disulphide, with a simple wick igniter
 (C) cellophane rolled tightly together and soaked with glycerin, with a simple wick igniter
 (D) a wax mold with potassium chlorate and a sugar mixture, with a length of safety fuse as an igniter

89. Those items used to produce brilliant light for illumination, or various smokes (colored) for signaling purposes, are referred to as:
 (A) lacrimates
 (B) incendiaries
 (C) pyrotechnics
 (D) photoflash powder

90. The best feature used to identify most pyrotechnic items is:
 (A) vent or emission holes on the outside of the container
 (B) red paint with white striping
 (C) red circles with blue painted circles
 (D) black paint on one half and white on the other half

91. Another name for tear gas is:
 (A) picric acid
 (B) lacrimate
 (C) trinitrotoluene
 (D) ammonium nitrate

92. The majority of military lacrimates have the symbols:
 (A) SN or NS or SN/NS on the can
 (B) ML or LM or ML/LM on the can
 (C) TG or GT or TG/MN on the can
 (D) CN or CS or CN/DM on the can

93. The combination of oil of valerium, sulfuric acid, and zinc straps are used as:

   (A) hoax bombs
   (B) pyrotechnics
   (C) stink bombs
   (D) lacrimates

94. Stink bombs are used mostly against:

   (A) police stations and vehicles
   (B) business establishments
   (C) public institutions
   (D) sports arenas

95. Stink bombs should be approached with caution because:

   (A) high gas pressure may be involved
   (B) they may contain nitroglycerin
   (C) small amounts of dynamite are often used
   (D) the top may be composed of a plastic explosive

96. Hoax bombs are:

   (A) just as dangerous as real bombs
   (B) often encountered by police
   (C) capable of small explosions
   (D) usually practical jokes

97. Hoax bombs usually contain:

   (A) motor oil
   (B) inert materials
   (C) valerium oil
   (D) sawdust

98. Hoax bombs are usually designed to:

   (A) extort valuables
   (B) decoy authorities
   (C) create panic
   (D) scare the victim

99. Of all systems a police officer will encounter, perhaps the most dangerous is the:

   (A) electrical fuse
   (B) friction fuse
   (C) chemical fuse
   (D) thermal fuse

100. The science that must be learned before teaching the fusing and firing systems in military munitions is:

(A) ballistics
(B) physics
(C) chemistry
(D) mathematics

KEY

QUES.	ANS.	PAGE	QUES.	ANS.	PAGE
1.	B	36	23.	C	45
2.	B	36	24.	A	45
3.	D	37	25.	C	45
4.	A	37	26.	B	46
5.	C	38	27.	D	46
6.	B	38	28.	B	47
7.	D	38	29.	A	47
8.	C	39	30.	C	47
9.	A	39	31.	C	47
10.	D	39	32.	A	48
11.	B	39	33.	C	48
12.	D	39,40	34.	B	48
13.	B	40	35.	C	49
14.	C	40	36.	D	49
15.	A	40	37.	A	49
16.	B	42	38.	C	49
17.	D	42	39.	D	50
18.	D	42	40.	D	50
19.	C	42	41.	B	51
20.	A	45	42.	A	51
21.	B	45	43.	C	51
22.	D	45	44.	A	51

QUES.	ANS.	PAGE	QUES.	ANS.	PAGE
45.	D	51	68.	A	65
46.	C	53	69.	C	67
47.	A	54	70.	B	68
48.	B	54	71.	C	68
49.	C	54	72.	A	70
50.	D	54	73.	B	77
51.	D	54	74.	D	78
52.	B	54	75.	C	80
53.	C	59	76.	B	84
54.	A	60	77.	A	84
55.	C	60	78.	C	84
56.	D	60	79.	B	85
57.	C	61	80.	A	85
58.	A	63	81.	D	85
59.	C	63	82.	C	85
60.	D	63	83.	B	85
61.	B	64	84.	C	85
62.	D	64	85.	D	85
63.	B	64	86.	A	85
64.	D	65	87.	C	89
65.	D	65	88.	D	89
66.	A	65	89.	C	90
67.	C	65	90.	A	90

SECTION V

1. Today many electrical power sources in explosive devices have been:

    (A) double-fused
    (B) dipped in nitro
    (C) miniaturized
    (D) booby-trapped

2. There are many power sources furnishing electrical power to explosives devices. Not a common source is:

    (A) chemical cells
    (B) thermal cells
    (C) a heat source
    (D) sulfuric acid

3. A police officer who is about to attempt to disarm an electrical circuit should:

    (A) remove his clothing
    (B) record his actions
    (C) ground himself
    (D) wear rubber gloves

4. The least likely type power source to be found in an electrical bomb is:

    (A) chemical
    (B) friction
    (C) thermal
    (D) heat

5. Two dissimilar metals combined with an electrolyte will create a/an:

    (A) explosion
    (B) ground
    (C) detonation
    (D) current

6. The common dry cell battery is an example of a:

    (A) chemical power source
    (B) light power source
    (C) magnetic power source
    (D) friction power source

7. The type battery consisting of two unlike metals, a dry salt electrolyte, and an incendiary mixture is known as a:
   (A) chemical cell
   (B) heat cell
   (C) thermal cell
   (D) friction cell

8. Which of the below is not a source of power for explosive devices:
   (A) vibration
   (B) light
   (C) pressure
   (D) magnets

9. The type switch consisting of a small ball bearing resting in an insulated material that, when tilted, causes the ball to roll across a set of contacts completing a circuit is known as a:
   (A) knife switch
   (B) ball switch
   (C) toggle switch
   (D) reed switch

10. Which of the below is not a type switch found in an electrical circuit of an explosive device:
    (A) micro
    (B) reed
    (C) clock
    (D) magnetic

11. Acids that are hypergolic in nature will cause certain chemicals to:
    (A) rapidly corrode metal
    (B) burst into flames
    (C) deteriorate and become harmless
    (D) explode with great force

12. The most widely used chemical acid is:
    (A) nitric
    (B) sulphuric
    (C) cupric chloride
    (D) acetone

13. Perhaps the easiest place to obtain sulphuric acid from is:
    (A) solder
    (B) oven cleaners
    (C) an automobile battery
    (D) tear gas cannisters

106

14. The use of chemical action as a means of initiation is particularly prevalent as a/an:

    (A) initiators for mechanical action
    (B) example of electrolytic action
    (C) triode for firing thyration
    (D) delay mechanism

15. A corrosive chemical often used in various delay fuses to eat through a wire which is holding a spring-loading firing pin to fire a stab-sensitive primer mixture is:

    (A) picric acid
    (B) sulphuric acid
    (C) acetone acid
    (D) cupric acid

16. Acetone is used in long delay fusing systems to:

    (A) create fire and heat
    (B) soften a plastic or celluloid
    (C) corrode and eat away metal
    (D) create metal fatigue

17. A factor that controls the effectiveness of acetone as a delay mechanism is the:

    (A) temperature
    (B) electrolytic response
    (C) thyration firing
    (D) type current
        firing release system

18. Not one of the four main systems used to fire a detonator is:

    (A) friction
    (B) electrical current
    (C) pressure release
    (D) chemical action

19. The initial action that starts the function of the fusing system is known as the:

    (A) initiating action
    (B) operation mechanism
    (C) fatigue factor
    (D) incendiary device

20. A sympathetic detonation is where:

    (A) an explosive device explodes after apparently being disarmed
    (B) one explosion causes a nearby explosive to detonate
    (C) a hoax explosive device is connected to a real explosive
    (D) a bomb is prepared in retaliation for a wrongdoing

107

21. Once access is gained to any device, the most important step then is to be able to:

 (A) recognize the initiating or triggering actions which will fire the mechanism
 (B) determine the mechanism responsible for the withdrawal
 (C) recognize the type explosive used as a main or auxiliary charge
 (D) initiate non-essential elements necessary for proper defusing

22. The first step or action which will cause the normal firing train to explode or ignite a device is the:

 (A) defusing action
 (B) collapsing action
 (C) cannonball action
 (D) initiating action

23. Which of the below is not a common method for triggering an explosive device:

 (A) pressure
 (B) pull
 (C) tilt
 (D) tumble

24. Rendering delayed time explosive devices harmless is particularly dangerous because of the:

 (A) unknown time element
 (B) small size of the explosive
 (C) high power explosives used
 (D) unknown triggering devices

25. Most crudely improvised timers will have a maximum delay of:

 (A) 11 hours
 (B) 24 hours
 (C) 12 hours
 (D) 36 hours

26. Certain military demolition or sabotage clocks have been known to run as high as:

 (A) 96 hours
 (B) 2 days
 (C) 5 days
 (D) 120 days

27. Chemical delay methods of initiating an explosive device work on the general principle of:

   (A) acid generating an electrical charge
   (B) an acid eating away a material
   (C) two chemicals combining to create an explosion
   (D) a negative charge reacting to a positive charge

28. Three sticks of dynamite, two lengths of electric wire, an electric blasting cap, and usually two alligator clips comprise a/an:

   (A) auto bomb
   (B) land mine
   (C) book bomb
   (D) open-hatch bomb

29. Most professional criminals will attach the dynamite for an auto bomb:

   (A) directly on the engine by the carburetor
   (B) inside the vehicle under the driver's seat
   (C) on the fire wall on the driver's side
   (D) next to the gasoline tank

30. The "booby-trap book" explosive commonly uses a/an:

   (A) electrical release device
   (B) pressure release device
   (C) chemical release device
   (D) friction release device

31. Police may encounter military grenades. Most grenades from the time thrown until explosion have a delay of about:

   (A) 4-5 seconds
   (B) 1-2 seconds
   (C) 2-3 seconds
   (D) 7-8 seconds

32. High explosive hand grenades usually contain:

   (A) 6-8 ounces of high explosive filler
   (B) 3-4 ounces of high explosive filler
   (C) 10-12 ounces of high explosive filler
   (D) 12-15 ounces of high explosive filler

33. The lethal bursting radius of a high explosive hand grenade is usually:

   (A) 25 feet
   (B) 50 feet
   (C) 100 feet
   (D) 250 feet

34. The danger bursting radius of a high explosive hand grenade is usually:

   (A)   300 feet
   (B)   150 feet
   (C)   1000 feet
   (D)   500 feet

35. A military gas capable of producing injuries or death is classified as a:

   (A)   physiological gas
   (B)   sickening gas
   (C)   vomiting gas
   (D)   casualty gas

36. War gases are usually classified by their:

   (A)   active contents
   (B)   pharmaceutical brand
   (C)   physiological actions
   (D)   inventor or founder

37. Phosgene and diphosgene are:

   (A)   nerve gas
   (B)   choking gas
   (C)   tear gases
   (D)   vomiting gases

38. Choking gases attack the:

   (A)   stomach
   (B)   kidneys
   (C)   respiratory tract
   (D)   brain

39. Perhaps the most lethal gas is:

   (A)   blister
   (B)   choking
   (C)   blood
   (D)   nerve

40. A gas used to cause serious casualties and not necessarily kill individuals is:

   (A)   tear
   (B)   vomiting
   (C)   blister
   (D)   nerve

41. Chloracetophenone is another name for:

    (A) tear gas
    (B) white phosphorus gas
    (C) blister gas
    (D) nerve gas

42. Two common household items, when combined, form a very dangerous, even deadly gas. They are:

    (A) ammonia and milk
    (B) bleach and vinegar
    (C) vinegar and baking soda
    (D) bleach and black pepper

43. One of the easiest methods of improvising a toxic gas is to:

    (A) burn salt and baking soda in a frying pan
    (B) heat ammonia in a saucepan over a very low flame
    (C) burn common white sugar in a frying pan
    (D) drip dry-cleaning fluid on a hot surface

44. Another word for self-igniting or spontaneously inflammable is:

    (A) kaolinite
    (B) hicetubique
    (C) hypergolic
    (D) eugenic

45. Rags soaked in motor oil will ignite rapidly if exposed to:

    (A) battery acid
    (B) ammonia
    (C) sulphur
    (D) common sugar

46. Flowers of sulphur heated with iron filings will produce an odor of:

    (A) flowers
    (B) bad fish
    (C) rotten eggs
    (D) cooked bacon

47. Should a police officer discover a suspected military chemical munition, he should first:

    (A) call a military disposal unit
    (B) notify his district or unit
    (C) evacuate the area
    (D) move it to a safe area

111

48. The cannon balls used in the Civil War were:
   (A) for the most part harmless solid shot
   (B) solid shot and required external propellants
   (C) mostly duds, over three quarters never firing
   (D) most often filled with a highly explosive bursting shot

49. If Civil War munitions are being transported for disposal, they should be carried:
   (A) under water
   (B) in wooden crates
   (C) inside sand bags
   (D) by rail

50. Which of the below agencies would be least likely to employ clandestine or sabotage devices:
   (A) racial groups
   (B) military engineers
   (C) police
   (D) rival labor groups

51. Probably the most common container for a sabotage type exploding device is:
   (A) pipe and tubing
   (B) hollowed out books
   (C) cigar boxes
   (D) glass bottles

52. Bomb disposal personnel should remember:
   (A) if given enough time all devices can be rendered harmless
   (B) a basic knowledge is required to construct a bomb
   (C) it is possible to construct devices that cannot be rendered safe
   (D) most explosive devices are manufactured for criminal acts

53. The disposal operation for a bomb or device should:
   (A) involve at least two men
   (B) where possible, be done alone
   (C) should seldom be done alone
   (D) be exploded remotely, if possible

54. By using a shotgun, access has often been gained into suspected packages. This method has been used to destroy or merely puncture the device to look inside. Success using this method was approximately:
   (A) 25%
   (B) 50%
   (C) 75%
   (D) 90%

55. The main purpose of the shotgun de-armer method is to:

    (A)   detonate the main charge
    (B)   gain access to a package by missing the main charge
    (C)   destroy the timing device
    (D)   sever electrical wires

56. After access has been gained to a suspected package, one effective method used to prevent the movement of a mechanical device, such as a movable plunger or clock, is:

    (A)   Plaster of Paris and water
    (B)   scotch or plastic tape
    (C)   vinegar or baking soda
    (D)   kerosene or rubbing alcohol

57. Before cutting the wires leading to or from any suspected device:

    (A)   immerse the device in water for at least one hour
    (B)   x-ray or fluoroscope the package
    (C)   all circuits should be thoroughly traced
    (D)   separate the main charge from the detonator

58. When cutting wires in a suspected device, only one wire should be cut and taped at a time. Beware of:

    (A)   wires that have their markings removed
    (B)   wires without insulation
    (C)   wires made of molded lead or similar alloys
    (D)   a double strand contained in what appears to be a single strand insulator

59. One method used to lower the potential of certain electrical batteries found in suspected devices is to:

    (A)   spray with alcohol
    (B)   apply or inject a freezing material
    (C)   soak in room temperature water
    (D)   coat the terminals with thick oil

60. When an explosive device is to be submerged in a liquid in hope of rendering it safe, the liquid should be:

    (A)   water
    (B)   oil
    (C)   kerosene
    (D)   milk

61. The method of trying to render safe an explosive device whereby a fine nitric acid spray is directed against a metallic container is referred to as:
    (A) trepanning
    (B) freezing
    (C) separating
    (D) re-routing

62. Once access is gained to a device containing high explosives, steam is often used to melt the explosive into a water-like mass. This technique should always be done:
    (A) at close quarters and using very high pressure steam
    (B) on a periodic basis over at least 24 hours
    (C) after the explosive device has been disarmed
    (D) remotely and once begun, not stopped until the process is complete

63. The best method for police to follow after receiving a bomb threat is to:
    (A) verify the source
    (B) evaluate its authenticity
    (C) check it out as fully as possible
    (D) have the call traced if possible

64. When evacuation of an area is necessary, it is best to:
    (A) tell the public it is a civil defense drill
    (B) tell the public the real reason
    (C) not let the public know the actual reason
    (D) not let the public use telephones in the area

65. In setting up an evacuation of an area, it is not wise to have:
    (A) volunteer rescue squad with general background training
    (B) local fire departments and rescue squad available
    (C) local utilities shut off (gas, electric, and fuel)
    (D) search parties move suspected device out of the area

66. Least important to record when receiving a telephone call involving a bomb scare is the:
    (A) exact language
    (B) accent
    (C) officer's name
    (D) time

67. Evacuation of an area should begin:
    (A) as soon as experienced personnel arrive
    (B) the minute a call is received
    (C) within a reasonable amount of time
    (D) as soon as facilities for evacuees are provided

68. Once an explosive or suspected device has been located in a building, it is best, immediately, to do all the following except:

   (A)   disarm device
   (B)   venting of device
   (C)   baffling procedures
   (D)   taping of windows

69. When an explosive device is found to exist, the fewest number of people possible should be utilized for the protective process, primarily:

   (A)   to minimize confusion
   (B)   for safety reasons
   (C)   for effective searching
   (D)   to eliminate duplication

70. Another name for sandbagging the wall adjacent to an explosive device to prevent blast and shock damage is:

   (A)   taping
   (B)   baffling
   (C)   venting
   (D)   buttressing

71. When an explosive device is discovered and mattresses or other materials are placed around the device to minimize the blast and fragment damage, we have a procedure known as:

   (A)   baffling
   (B)   buttressing
   (C)   venting
   (D)   taping

72. The number of personnel assigned to a bomb squad should be determined by all except

   (A)   size of unit
   (B)   population
   (C)   frequency of incidents
   (D)   facilities available

73. Police officers should not be committed to demolition or bomb disposal duty without:

   (A)   military service
   (B)   prior civilian training
   (C)   military bomb training
   (D)   actual field experience

74. Men assigned to bomb disposal work should be closely evaluated in many areas. Least important is:

(A) I. Q.
(B) seniority
(C) temperament
(D) aptitude

75. Training for bomb disposal officers should consist of all of the below except:

(A) frequent meetings with other bomb units
(B) actual demolition work
(C) self-evaluation
(D) training aid problems

76. A bomb disposal area is often called a:

(A) football field
(B) morgue
(C) cemetery
(D) hot spot

77. The method which will fire a device on the application of water pressure is known as a/an:

(A) anti-probe circuit
(B) acoustic circuit
(C) hydrostatic system
(D) proximity system

78. A disposal area for explosives and devices should, if possible, be located:

(A) in the center of the town or city
(B) at the perimeter of the town or city
(C) far from a town or city
(D) in abandoned coal or iron mines

79. The most important factor to remember when transporting a live bomb is:

(A) never ride in the same vehicle
(B) know the type bomb involved
(C) avoid streets with bumps
(D) wear protective clothing

80. Protective material to ward off and offer protection against bombs and devices is often made from:

(A) woven nylon in several layers
(B) woven copper cable
(C) woven silk in several layers
(D) woven flexible steel cable

81. A danger in using an x-ray or fluoroscope for examining a suspected bomb or device is:
    (A) it will not penetrate lead
    (B) the close proximity required
    (C) it may initiate the explosive
    (D) continued use may affect the user

82. A device placed into an explosive unit designed to function the mechanism on any attempt to move it is called a/an:
    (A) brisance mechanism
    (B) cavitation device
    (C) shrapnel fuse
    (D) anti-disturbance device

83. A device is set to go off when lifted due to the utilization of a special device called a/an:
    (A) arming delay
    (B) baffle
    (C) anti-lift mechanism
    (D) timing disc

84. A feature or device which prevents the removal of a fuse or triggering mechanism from an explosive device is called a/an:
    (A) anti-withdrawal device
    (B) timing disc
    (C) squib
    (D) pineapple

85. Munitions that are in functional condition to work are referred as being:
    (A) boostered
    (B) armed
    (C) hypergolic
    (D) fused

86. The removal of safety devices or arranging components from a safe condition to a state of readiness for initiation is known as:
    (A) arming
    (B) fusing
    (C) boostering
    (D) buttressing

87. Arming delays are usually installed in explosive devices to allow the perpetrator:
    (A) to complete all connections
    (B) to arm a device
    (C) to withdraw from the area
    (D) a margin of safety

88. When an explosive device has been started and is moving towards the firing time, it is said to be:

    (A) in a state of brisance
    (B) armed and functioning
    (C) in a state of sympathetic detonation
    (D) at its rubicon

89. A material used to defeat an explosive shock wave such as a wall or screen is called a:

    (A) cavitation
    (B) desensitizer
    (C) baffle
    (D) cordtex

90. Blasting caps are normally fired by safety fuse, electric current, or:

    (A) bursting charge
    (B) cavitation
    (C) deflagration
    (D) chemical action

91. Containers for blasting caps are usually constructed of copper, aluminum, or:

    (A) paper
    (B) plastic
    (C) stainless steel
    (D) eremite

92. Blasting time fuses consist of fabric cord containing:

    (A) black powder
    (B) nitroglycerine
    (C) a bursting charge
    (D) a desensitizer

93. Another name for time fuse is:

    (A) safety fuse
    (B) B. D. fuse
    (C) cavitation fuse
    (D) bursting fuse

94. Time for blasting time fuse is usually:

    (A) 5-10 seconds per foot
    (B) 10-15 seconds per foot
    (C) 15-20 seconds per foot
    (D) 30-45 seconds per foot

95. In a firing train of an explosive, the order is usually:

   (A) primer, detonator, booster, and main charge
   (B) detonator, primer, booster, and main charge
   (C) booster, primer, detonator, and main charge
   (D) primer, booster, detonator, and main charge

96. In explosives, brisance refers to the:

   (A) detonation of the main charge
   (B) propelling blast from the main charge
   (C) degree of shattering effect exerted by the explosive
   (D) arming delay working and functional

97. Sand bags or loose sand poured against walls or around an explosive device is known as:

   (A) cavitating
   (B) buttressing
   (C) baffling
   (D) desensitizing

98. A small arms cartridge made of brass containing the primer, propellant, and projectile is known as a:

   (A) blasting cap
   (B) booby trap
   (C) cartridge
   (D) firing device

99. TNT melted and poured into a bomb case for hardening is a method of loading referred to as:

   (A) pour loading
   (B) cast loading
   (C) counter loading
   (D) prime loading

100. Another name for a firing pin is a/an:

   (A) detonator
   (B) ignition train
   (C) cocked striker
   (D) fuse

QUES.	ANS.	PAGE	QUES.	ANS.	PAGE
1.	C	96	23.	D	112,113
2.	D	101	24.	A	113
3.	C	101	25.	C	114
4.	B	100	26.	D	114
5.	D	101	27.	B	117
6.	A	101	28.	A	132
7.	C	101	29.	C	132
8.	A	102	30.	B	134
9.	B	103	31.	A	171
10.	D	103	32.	B	171
11.	B	104	33.	A	171
12.	B	104	34.	B	171
13.	C	104	35.	D	178
14.	D	104	36.	C	178
15.	D	104	37.	B	178
16.	B	105	38.	C	178
17.	A	105	39.	D	179
18.	C	109	40.	C	179
19.	A	109	41.	A	180
20.	B	111	42.	B	181
21.	A	112	43.	D	181
22.	D	112	44.	C	182

QUES.	ANS.	PAGE	QUES.	ANS.	PAGE
45.	A	182	68.	A	245
46.	C	182	69.	B	245
47.	C	185	70.	D	245
48.	D	189	71.	A	245
49.	A	201	72.	D	246
50.	C	202,203	73.	D	247
51.	A	203	74.	B	247
52.	C	212	75.	C	248
53.	A	215	76.	C	254
54.	D	217	77.	C	121
55.	B	218	78.	B	254
56.	A	232	79.	A	258
57.	C	232	80.	D	258
58.	D	232	81.	B	266
59.	B	232,233	82.	D	272
60.	B	233	83.	C	272
61.	A	233	84.	A	272
62.	D	233	85.	B	272
63.	C	239	86.	A	272
64.	C	239	87.	D	272
65.	D	239	88.	B	272
66.	C	243	89.	C	272
67.	B	243	90.	D	273

SECTION VI

1. In an explosive, the mixtures used in the manufacture of an explosive device or the explosion itself is also known as a:
    (A) desensitizer
    (B) compound
    (C) deflagration
    (D) trepan mixture

2. An improvised explosive using fuels and oxidizers is also known as a:
    (A) cavity core
    (B) Greek fire train
    (C) timbering bomb
    (D) contrived explosive

3. A cook-off is an explosive or munition that:
    (A) upon initiation fails to fire but due to excessive heat will eventually function at an unexpected time
    (B) requires detonation by several blasting caps, one at each end of the explosive
    (C) has desensitized and must be destroyed by fire
    (D) fails to explode and burns with a flash

4. Primacord or detonating cord is also known as:
    (A) coorex
    (B) cordtex
    (C) cotedex
    (D) crotex

5. In disposal of explosives, counter charge means:
    (A) exploding two charges at the same time
    (B) a series of explosions each following the other
    (C) detonating one charge by placing it next to another
    (D) a small charge detonating several large charges

6. E.O.D. is a military abbreviation for:
    (A) explosive oxidizer detonation
    (B) explosive ordnance disposal
    (C) explode on direction
    (D) explosive ordinarily detonated

7. Examples of desensitizers used to reduce the sensitivity of an explosive are:
    (A) kerosene, milk, water, fugee
    (B) baby powder, nylon, and water
    (C) ice, gasoline, water, rayon
    (D) acetone, sawdust, starch, gelatin

8. Cordtex and primacord are called:

   (A) desensitizers
   (B) firing pins
   (C) detonating cord
   (D) blasting caps

9. The best example of a detonator is a:

   (A) blasting cap
   (B) firing pin
   (C) hypergolic
   (D) fougasse

10. Low explosives are said to:

    (A) detonate
    (B) desensitize
    (C) photo-flash
    (D) deflagrate

11. Nitroglycerine is desensitized by adding:

    (A) sawdust
    (B) oil
    (C) gelatin
    (D) water

12. E.S.P. is a military abbreviation for:

    (A) extra sensory perception
    (B) electrical safing procedure
    (C) explosion safety procedure
    (D) explosive striker plan

13. An expression used by experts to warn people in the vicinity of danger an explosion is about to occur is:

    (A) "fire in the hole"
    (B) "run for your life"
    (C) "hey Rube"
    (D) "blitzkrug"

14. A military term referring to an improvised incendiary or explosive device, designed for use against personnel, usually buried, is called a:

    (A) hell box
    (B) fuzee
    (C) high order device
    (D) fougasse

126

15. Nearly all explosives require an oxidizer to provide oxygen and a fuel to:

    (A) incite fragmentation
    (B) sustain burning
    (C) initiate a device
    (D) prime the charge

16. A fuse can be chemical, electric, or:

    (A) fragmenting
    (B) improvised
    (C) mechanical
    (D) delay

17. A fuzee is a:

    (A) burning flare or pyrotechnic device used as a warning device
    (B) fuse used to initiate dynamite
    (C) link in the chain of initiation for high military explosives
    (D) liquid fuel used in rocket propulsion

18. The bomb disposal term "gag" most nearly means:

    (A) a false bomb threat
    (B) to immobilize movable parts of an explosive device
    (C) people are killed in a terrorist bombing
    (D) to explode a large amount of explosives

19. A hand operated generator used to electrically initiate blasting caps in explosive operations is often called a:

    (A) hoax machine
    (B) Lucifer loop
    (C) hell box
    (D) initiator

20. The term "high order" means:

    (A) the order in which explosives are to be detonated
    (B) detonate a specific device first
    (C) high grade explosives are to be detonated
    (D) a successful and complete detonation

21. Hygroscopic means most nearly:

    (A) the ability to readily absorb and retain moisture
    (B) a low grade explosive used in hand grenades, etc.
    (C) a method of self-ignition
    (D) a fusing system utilizing an incorporated delty

127

22. Hypergolic means most nearly:
    - (A) a hoax bomb
    - (B) self-igniting
    - (C) inert materials
    - (D) a low grade fuel

23. The primer or detonator of an explosive device is known as a/an:
    - (A) propellant
    - (B) powder train
    - (C) initiator
    - (D) oxidizer

24. A low order explosion usually:
    - (A) utilizes low grade explosives
    - (B) performed by bomb experts
    - (C) fires a solid or liquid projectile
    - (D) fails to detonate properly

25. Mustard gas is:
    - (A) derived from table mustard
    - (B) a blistering agent
    - (C) made from coal-tar
    - (D) a product of World War II

26. An oxidizer supplies:
    - (A) fuel
    - (B) oxygen
    - (C) internal combustion
    - (D) initiation

27. A slang term for a dynamite bomb or hand grenade is:
    - (A) pineapple
    - (B) pop-corner
    - (C) Daisy-May
    - (D) Baby Ruth

28. A plastic bomb is often used by terrorists because of its:
    - (A) ease of ignition
    - (B) cost
    - (C) flexibility
    - (D) low order effect

29. Plastic explosives range in color from:
    - (A) blue to green
    - (B) white to red
    - (C) white to blue
    - (D) yellow to white

30. A very rapid burning time fuse is often called:

    (A)   quick-match fuse
    (B)   oxidizing fuse
    (C)   plastic fuse
    (D)   squib fuse

31. Safety fuse contains a:

    (A)   no explosive powder
    (B)   core of cellophane
    (C)   continuous core of black powder
    (D)   liquid core of nitroglycerine

32. A solvent used to soften and dissolve TNT is:
    (A)   graphite
    (B)   acetone
    (C)   water
    (D)   gasoline

33. A small pencil-like tube containing black powder used to transmit a flame or ignite certain devices is called a:

    (A)   fougasse
    (B)   blasting cap
    (C)   dundee
    (D)   squib

34. A detonation where one explosion causes another device to explode is often said to have been a/an:

    (A)   trepan explosion
    (B)   sympathetic detonation
    (C)   pyrotechnic detonation
    (D)   improvised initiation

35. In bomb disposal work, the act of timbering most nearly means:
    (A)   placing wooden beams into an excavation for support
    (B)   cutting the fuse to an explosion device
    (C)   an act of sabotage
    (D)   blowing up a house or apartment building

36. To cut through or gain access or entrance by cutting, sawing, or corrosive acid action is called:
    (A)   timbering
    (B)   trepanning
    (C)   squibbing
    (D)   initiation

37. U.X.B. is a military abbreviation for:
    (A) underwater bomb—unknown
    (B) underwater enemy bomb
    (C) unexploded nitroglycerine bomb
    (D) unexploded bomb

38. Demolition personnel should not uncoil wires or use electric blasting caps in the vicinity of:
    (A) major roads or highways
    (B) radio-frequency transmitters
    (C) schools or playgrounds
    (D) military bases

39. Electric blasting caps, either singly or when connected in a series circuit, should be tested by a
    (A) frequency modulator
    (B) circuit breaker
    (C) blasting galvanometer
    (D) electric transformer

40. When using fuse to detonate an explosive device, never use less than:
    (A) 6 feet
    (B) 10 feet
    (C) 15 feet
    (D) 25 feet

41. When lighting the fuse of an explosive:
    (A) use a match
    (B) wear protective goggles
    (C) be in an open area
    (D) do not have the explosive in your hand

42. A suspected package should not be submerged in water because of the:
    (A) conductivity of electric circuits and a possible reaction with chemical agents
    (B) toxic fumes may be released when exposed to water
    (C) a mechanical or chemical explosion may occur when a metallic object is subjected with an oxidizer
    (D) water contains hydrogen, a chemical that excites certain other compounds

43. If nitroglycerine is transported it should be in a:
    (A) copper container
    (B) stainless steel container
    (C) plastic container
    (D) silver container

44. When dealing with suspected packages, disposal personnel should:
    (A) always work alone
    (B) not cut two wires at the same time
    (C) accept identification markings as accurate
    (D) not use metallic tools in a close proximity

45. When working on a suspected package, don't wear:
    (A) cotton clothing
    (B) nylon clothing
    (C) rayon clothing
    (D) silk clothing

46. When working on a suspected package, do not work near steam pipes, belts or pulleys, or moving wheels, primarily because:
    (A) clothing may get caught or hooked
    (B) there is a danger of static charges
    (C) air waves may detonate the device
    (D) a galvanic reaction may occur

47. X-rays should not be used on a suspected package where:
    (A) the outer container is metal
    (B) a specific detonation time is known
    (C) time is not essential
    (D) a clock work mechanism is heard to be active

48. Perhaps the most dangerous form of extraneous electrical energy to be considered when firing blasting circuits electrically is:
    (A) lightning
    (B) static electricity
    (C) radio frequency energy
    (D) transmission lines

49. Conditions not capable of causing a high accumulation of static charge is:
    (A) snow storms
    (B) nylon clothing
    (C) dust storms
    (D) copper wiring

50. Blasting near high tension wires should be done with:
    (A) electric wire
    (B) detonating cord
    (C) .25 amp wire
    (D) sound waves

KEY

QUES.	ANS.	PAGE	QUES.	ANS.	PAGE
1.	B	274	26.	B	278
2.	D	274	27.	A	278
3.	A	274	28.	C	278
4.	B	274	29.	D	279
5.	C	274	30.	A	279
6.	B	274	31.	C	280
7.	D	274	32.	B	280
8.	C	275	33.	D	280
9.	A	275	34.	B	281
10.	D	275	35.	A	281
11.	C	275	36.	B	281
12.	B	275	37.	D	281
13.	A	275	38.	B	288
14.	D	276	39.	C	288
15.	B	276	40.	A	288
16.	C	276	41.	D	289
17.	A	276	42.	A	290
18.	B	276	43.	C	290
19.	C	276,277	44.	D	290,291
20.	D	277	45.	B	292
21.	A	277	46.	B	292
22.	B	277	47.	D	292
23.	C	277	48.	A	293
24.	D	278	49.	C	294,295
25.	B	278	50.	B	297

This Study Guide contains more than 590 Civil Service Type Questions and Answers.

★ 242 Questions and Answers are based on and indexed by page number to the text, Bombs and Bombings, by Thomas G. Brodie. Mr. Brodie also wrote our Study Guide Questions.

★ Lieut. Ralph E. Hendel has written 350 Questions and Answers based on and indexed to the text, Explosives and Bomb Disposal Guide by Robert R. Lenz.

DAVIS PUBLISHING CO. INC.

250 POTRERO STREET
SANTA CRUZ, CALIFORNIA 95060
(408) 423-4968